God's Greatest Gift

A True Story

by Chad Godfrey

Illustrations by John Cornwell

Beehive Publishing
1998

ᔈ For ᔈ

Keith, Troy, Merlin, Floyd, Barbara, Helen, Ruth, and Fred

God's Greatest Gift
by Chad Godfrey

© Beehive Publishing Ph. (801) 288-1133
P.O. Box 71113, Salt Lake City, Utah 84121
First Printing October 1998
ISBN # 0-9660670-0-2
Library of Congress Catalogue Card Number: 97-94675

Distributor: Evans Books
Salt Lake City, Utah

↩ Table of Contents ↪

❧ AUTHOR'S NOTE ❧

This book is based on a true story. It spans nearly a decade from 1931 to 1939, but the main events occurred around Christmas 1938. In places, the time line was compressed to accommodate events.

The Yeates family lived in northern Utah with their eight children. Melba and Leo Yeates were my grandparents. Their seventh child, Ruth, is my mother.

This story is written through the eyes of the eldest child, Keith; yet it's really a composite view taken from memories of several family members who knew and loved "Meb." Keith reflects insights gleaned over many years from later conversations, thus he sometimes speaks from a third-person point of view.

I'm grateful to members of my family who supported or assisted the writing of this book, especially Aunt Priel, Uncle Troy, DeLynn Yeates, Sue Rampton, my mother Ruth, and my wife Pam. Special thanks go to Maxine Hanks.

❧ MAP OF NIBLEY AREA ❧

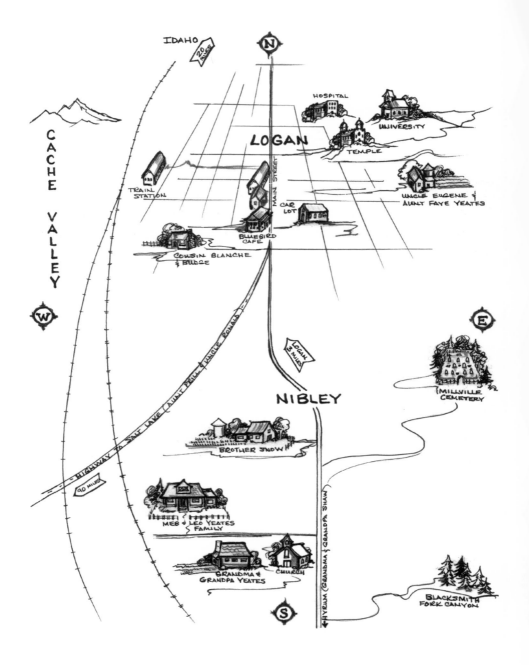

❧ PROLOGUE ❧

People are like presents. They're somewhat predictable, yet always hold a bit of mystery. Rarely do we know for certain what's inside. But eventually we learn. Probing outer layers usually leads to answers within.

In 1931, presents were precious. Money was scarce, so any gift was a sacrifice. The years during and after the Great Depression were dire times.

However, Christmas was important. The whole year led up to it. Our goal was to try and get ahead just enough to buy something, anything, for the holiday.

Even in the Depression, people splurged for the Yuletide season. There were jingle bells and chimes, colored lights and carolers—even a band played "Peace on earth, good will to men" on the street as trolley cars rolled by.

Usually, we stood outside on snowy sidewalks and looked through store windows. Without money, there was no reason to go inside. We gazed at wooden planes and puppets, trains, dolls, and wagons. These fueled our imaginations. At night I laid in bed listening to my two younger brothers yammer about cap guns, until I began to wish I had one just so I could shoot it as a signal to stop talking.

Every December, Dad took an extra job at the Logan Post Office to make a little Christmas money. Dad's brother Eugene was a banker, as well as the Logan postmaster. The title sounded important, but Uncle Eugene said his postal job was tedious. He had to stand all day listening to people talk about their mail while stamping and hand-sorting endless letters. Gene dreaded the holiday mail, so he told his supervisors he needed Dad's help. I think he just needed the company.

With his post office money, Dad bought presents. This usually meant that we got a Christmas stocking with something inside it besides dirty toes. Peering down into the bottom of our socks, we found hard tack candy and peanuts; if we were lucky, an apple or an orange rested on top. This was your basic Depression-era Christmas present. Ask anyone who was a kid in those days, and they'll describe the same scenario, give or take a lump of coal.

My mother bought fabric for pennies to sew flannel pajamas and nightgowns, cotton dresses, and trousers. One year she made us boys a plaid wool jacket; we wrestled for it every morning to see who would wear it to school.

Store-bought toys were rare, so we shared them. Mom and Dad managed to buy a toy now and then, though I never knew how they did it. (Unless Dad was selling whiskey and not telling; but he was far too religious for that.) I think they simply saved small change for months.

No matter how little we had, Mother and Dad made us feel important. Perhaps they were no different than any other hardworking parents during the Depression. Yet for some reason, they seemed happier than most folks. I guess they loved life, or each other. In any case, they loved us.

Those times were severe, but our home was a comforting place. Life was not so barren if you lived on a farm. Our meagerness seemed satisfying because we were rich in gifts of love; or maybe because we were just oblivious kids.

We didn't know existence was tenuous. We were young and indestructible, energized like rockets. As children, we thought life was perfect. We probably expected too much from Mom and Dad. We believed they were taking care of everything.

My parents absorbed all worries for us. My father was a good and sober man at a time when so many men were down and out. I believe he was genuinely happy. My mother was gentle and loving, her feelings tender and sincere.

Looking back, I cherish the gifts my parents gave with their hearts: the way Dad sang for us at night, or the way Mom tended to our needs.

I was only ten in 1931, but I remember it all as if it were yesterday. One family's struggle in the 1930s. I tell our story simply because it happened, because it matters to me. I want someone to understand. I suppose that's reason enough to write it.

Today, I see my mother like a gift, that perhaps we took for granted. No mystery to us, she simply embodied love. I realized this one Christmas as I watched my little sisters waving brand new mittens she had knitted; each pair was made from a different shade of yarn, like a vivid hue of her love.

But as the years passed and the decade declined, we learned there was more to Mother, and to life, than we ever suspected. We discovered new dimensions of life's most vital gifts.

⌘ ONE ⌘
Holidays

I'm not sure why, but winters were worse in the 1930s. All those stories the old folks tell about walking miles in snowdrifts aren't fables. Ask anyone who lived through that decade and they'll back me up: we saw some of the hardest winters on record.

In 1936, the snow was piled five feet high in downtown Logan. It took a sixty-horse-power caterpillar tractor to scrape Main Street—the biggest machine we had in those days. Folks plowed their own snowed-in country roads with teams of horses.

Maybe the harsh weather was caused by coal smoke hanging in thin winter air. Or maybe the earth really is growing warmer these days. Or everything just seemed more intense when we were children. Whatever the reason, those winter snows nearly buried us.

We dug our way out by making corridors, hills, and paths, sculpting a new winter landscape around us. Horse-drawn buggies and sleighs slid along narrow, deeply-drifted roads, while automobiles were stranded or moved in slow motion.

We lived on a farm in northern Utah, about 20 miles from the Idaho border. It was a collection of homesteads called Nibley.

Our wood frame farmhouse bustled with energy and life, a gathering place for both of my parents' families. At Christmas time, pine wreaths welcomed visitors to our wide country porch. Snow piled waist deep against the siding, spraying over window sills and across glass panes in wild patterns. At night, my oil lantern glowed softly in the darkness, illuminating millions of tiny ice crystals in the crisp winter air.

Christmas in 1931 was good, in spite of the Depression. Our holidays were always happy.

My father's name was Leo Yeates. My mother was Melba Shaw, but everybody called her "Meb." Petite and pretty, with dark brown hair and eyes, she was a mother of six and a talented homemaker at age 33.

"Meb, where do you want these onions and potatoes?" Dad would ask, coming up from the cellar.

"Leave them in the sink. I'll take care of them," she'd say.

"Meb, you're doing all the work," Grandma Shaw scolded. "Let me help."

"I'm fine," was Mom's usual response.

Mother went all out for Christmas dinner, even in the Depression years. She loved hosting parties, inviting people to sample her cooking. She wanted others to have a good time.

My mother could make a meal out of nothing. I know it sounds like an exaggeration, but some women are magicians when it comes to food. She combined ingredients mysteriously until a delicious new substance took form. Even in scarcity, my mother could conjure a feast.

My aunts still tell people today, "You've never seen food like Meb could make." Mother's great-grandmother was a chef for the Queen of England and her talent for fine cooking passed down from mother to daughter. My mother had the gift.

Between my aunts, Mama had plenty of help in the kitchen. This left me free to roam around and eavesdrop on conversations.

"I tell you, Leo, Hoover can't help us; I don't think anything short of war will end this depression," Uncle Eugene insisted.

"We've already seen the war to end all wars—we don't need another," Dad countered. "Hard work will set this country right."

"If people would put more faith in God and less in the almighty dollar, the world would be a lot better off." Cousin Budge figured God was the answer.

Dad was a fine-looking man, just five feet five inches tall with dark brown hair and eyes. He had a square jaw and a pleasant smile. At age 39, he was a farmer like his father.

On Christmas we always had a full house for dinner. There was Grandpa Shaw who had pockets full of lemon drops, and Grandma of course. Uncle Eugene and his wife. Aunt Priel who looked like Mother, small with dark hair, and her husband. Dad's sisters, Aunt Reva and Marvel, who lived nearby. Mom's favorite cousin, Blanche, and her husband, Budge, the town barber.

Dad's parents came too, Grandpa Fred and Annie Yeates. They lived up our road on the corner, next to the Nibley church which Grandpa helped build. Across the road stood the Nibley general store; this was downtown Nibley—where our road ended at a bigger road running north to Logan and south to Hyrum.

Mom's family, the Shaws, had lived in Hyrum for generations, where her grandparents had pioneered. Dad used to ride his horse over to Hyrum every Sunday just to see Mom.

"Meb was the prettiest girl in Hyrum," Dad always bragged, "and the best cook, too."

"I was the only girl in Hyrum," Mom quipped.

Mom and Dad believed humor was one of life's necessities, especially during the Depression. They managed to make Christmas fun, even in 1931.

After the stock market crash of 1929, most adults walked around with a permanent frown on their faces. Even my cousin Billy was unhappy because he put his entire fortune of five dollars in the bank and then couldn't get it back. He complained about it for years (in fact, he still complains about it today).

Everyone blamed President Hoover for the Depression, but the seeds were planted before, in the roaring '20s—a time of excess. High profits brought inflation and banks had no reserve funds. International instability and a growing lack of confidence caused shudders all over Wall Street. Once panic set in, everything started falling, like a house of cards.

I suppose any system is vulnerable to the possibility of a collapse. Growth is always a risk mode, reaching forward to move ahead.

President Hoover worked hard to cope with the Depression, but as a conservative, he didn't take risks and couldn't make a big difference.

Dad was always singing some ditty about Hoover. "Along came Hoover with his economic talk; you can't get a car so now ya gotta walk. Best thing to do is to do the best ya can, 'cause they sure made the devil when they made the first man."

In retrospect, 1931 was not so bad. We were healthy and happy.

Being the oldest, I was responsible for helping my younger siblings and doing the chores. My name is Keith. They say I'm the silent type. Like Dad, I worried about the farm, the weather, and the future.

After me came Troy and Mert, the wild pair. Mert's name was actually Merlin, like the magician. He loved to clown around. Troy was a talker who spoke for all of us. Maybe it was because he had red hair, while the rest of us had brown.

Next came Floyd and Barbara, two middle kids who liked to have fun but were not as rambunctious as Troy and Mert.

Helen was our baby (until two more babies came along). She grew to be like me—quiet, reserved, an observer. We held things in, not saying much.

When 1932 arrived, new hope appeared on the horizon; a democrat was elected president. Franklin D. Roosevelt promised the country a New Deal that would bring recovery from rampant unemployment. Most folks saw Roosevelt as a godsend.

Dad went about his farm chores singing the Roosevelt campaign song. "Happy days are here again, the skies above are clear again, we'll sing a song of cheer again, happy days are here again!"

It was hard not to join in singing as I did the milking. Even the cows' tails seemed to swish in rhythm.

We felt a difference that next Christmas. Not because we had any more money, which we didn't. Simple hope and optimism were in the air, lifting attitudes. Cousin Budge said the power of positive thinking could cure most anything.

On Christmas morning 1932, we tumbled out of bed and scampered into the living room, making a beeline to the tree. I don't why we were in such a hurry to eat hard tack candy and peanuts.

There stood our Christmas tree on its perennial spot, in front of the living room window. Draped in popcorn and hung with foil decorations, it looked happy. A huge, slightly bent aluminum star jumped out on top.

What we saw next was too good to be true. Three presents were waiting underneath: a rectangular box, a small round object, and a doll.

Mother picked up the doll. "This is for Barbara," she smiled, putting it into the child's hands.

The handmade doll had yellow yarn hair and a blue gingham dress. Barbara squeezed her dolly tightly around the neck.

"Jeepers, you're gonna strangle it," Mert kidded. Barbara clutched it even tighter.

Mert and Floyd looked at the rectangular box.

"I bet it's shoes," Mert guessed.

"Open it," Floyd urged. Mert tore open the box and pulled out a shiny black, wind-up locomotive.

"A train!" they both exclaimed. Dad winked at Mother.

Mert wound that train and ran it around the house about a hundred times before stopping. He nearly wore it out the first day.

The last present under the tree was for me and Troy. Small and round, it was wrapped in a piece of bright red cloth and tied with a white string.

Troy picked it up and untied the string. Then he slowly peeled off the cloth, like the skin of an orange.

It was a brand new baseball, autographed by Babe Ruth.

"Wow!" yelped Troy. "I'm gonna hit a home run!"

"How did you get it?" I asked Dad.

"We wanted to get you older boys something unique," Dad said.

"We sent away for it last summer," Mom explained.

Troy tossed it to me and I caught it.

"Not in the house, you two," Dad warned. We ran outside in the snow, throwing fast balls at each other until Troy hit me in the leg.

We were so excited we didn't care if it was a collector's item. Troy and I played with that ball every day for three years until we wore it out. Long after that ball was gone, I cherished the gift.

Later on that day in the warmth of our living room, Grandpa Shaw played patty cake with Barbara on the couch. Floyd sat in the big chair, waiting for dinner, bored. In the parlor, which my parents used as a bedroom, Mother was changing Helen's diaper. Troy flopped down on the oval living room rug, picking a comfortable spot to read the Sears & Roebuck catalogue. Grandma Shaw's hand-braided rag rugs covered our pinewood floors.

In the dining room, our round oak table was beginning to fill with food. A pot-bellied coal stove resting in the corner was our main source of heat, but today pans of hot rolls rested on top. The portraits of Grandpa and Grandma Yeates on the dining wall kept a watchful eye. Off to the right in the bedroom where we boys slept, Mert was sorting his baseball card collection.

Back in the kitchen, my aunts were buzzing like bees. The largest and brightest room, it occupied the back width of our house. Today, the kitchen was crowded and busy. I had to plaster myself against the far wall to stay out of the way. Six women were helping Mom get Christmas dinner ready. Everyone seemed to be talking at once.

"Do we have enough potatoes?"

"My goodness, smell that stuffing!"

"Watch out, the gravy's hot."

The smell of food revived Troy, who poked his head in the doorway.

"Keith, could you and Troy start setting the tables?" Mom asked me.

"Sure," I spoke for both of us. Troy made a face.

Today I counted 14 grownups and six kids. Dad rigged two extra tables in order to seat everybody: two tables for people and one to hold only food. He asked Mert to set up the chairs. "Just don't wreck anything," Dad warned.

When I finished placing mismatched china, borrowed plates, and silverware, I went back out to the living room.

Grandpa Shaw nudged me, "What did Leo pick for dinner?"

"A pheasant and a turkey," I grinned.

"Meb stuffed them with her pinenut dressing," Grandpa Yeates said, licking his lips. He walked into the kitchen to help hurry things up.

Troy and Mert were so anxious for Christmas dinner, they were getting silly. They chased each other around until they were dizzy and Mert tripped on the rug, nearly landing on one of the makeshift tables.

"You're gonna crash the table!" Grandpa Shaw threatened to send them outside. Barbara sat in Grandma Yeates' lap, still strangling her new doll. I took some scraps out to the barn for Brownie, our dog.

Finally, Dad and Uncle Eugene came through the kitchen door each carrying a platter of roasted turkey, spilling stuffing.

Blanche had hot rolls and Aunt Priel carried mashed potatoes with butter. Aunt Reva opened jars of fruit and jam that Mother had bottled the previous summer—raspberry, cherries, and peaches.

Mom carried steaming bowls of vegetables cooked in butter, with cream and seasoning.

"You sure use a lot of butter for somebody named Melba," Priel teased her.

"I could leave the carrots plain," Mother ventured.

"No, that's okay," Dad quickly reacted. "Did you make squash?"

"Yes," she smiled walking back into the kitchen. Her steamed squash was whipped smooth with cream and sweetened with a touch of applesauce.

Then came the pumpkin pie, peanut brittle, and a great big bowl of creamy white divinity. The makeshift food table was nearly overloaded. Troy counted 18 items, from turkey to candy.

I heard the sound of sawhorses creaking and nails pulling loose as the table began to sway under the weight of all that food. My aunts screamed while my uncles scrambled to grab the table before it went down. Somehow, as one end gave way, they barely managed to save it from crashing to the floor. Grabbing the long plywood top around its sides, Dad, Budge, Grandpa, and Eugene stood holding our table covered with platters and bowls sloshing their contents over the sides. No one knew quite what to do.

Mert and Troy started laughing so hard they couldn't stop. They got us all going.

"Ease it down to the floor," Dad instructed. The men set the table top onto the rug where it remained for the duration of our dinner.

"I don't mind eating off the floor," Aunt Reva consoled Mother.

We dished our plates from the floor and sat wherever we felt like sitting. Mert, Troy, Floyd, and I positioned ourselves around the plywood table, cross-legged on the rug.

"Indian style," Troy said.

Mother was embarrassed, but everything was delicious.

After dinner, we boys laid on the rug too full to do anything else.

"Are we going to see the Christmas lights?" I asked Dad.

"New Year's Eve," Dad promised. "Blanche and Budge invited us up to Logan for dinner."

"I'm not gonna eat until then," Troy announced.

"I wanna hear Dad yodel," Mert asserted, ready for action.

My dad could yodel like a pro. He had heard someone yodeling on the radio, then started singing along and really took to it. People would say "Yodel, Leo!" and he'd just yodel away like a Swiss goat herder.

It was a good release for all the energy in that food. Aunt Reva and Marvel and Uncle Eugene all began urging Dad on.

So Dad stood in the center of the living room and began yodeling at the top of his lungs. Mert did his best to imitate, not quite getting the hang of it. Everyone clapped to keep Dad going, faster and faster, yodeling louder and higher—until he finally collapsed into the chair, out of breath.

✑ TWO ✑
Meb

"**M**om, where's the iodine?" I yelled, stepping through the back door of the kitchen.

Mama was making bread, which was no small task. She made eight loaves every other day.

"Hush," Mom called quietly from the living room. "It's down in the cellar."

She was taking a break, rocking three-year-old Helen on her lap, humming a lullaby. By 1933, we kids were growing like dandelions. I was twelve now.

"Sorry," I whispered back. "I cut my hand." A touch of antiseptic would fix the spot where I had scratched myself on a tool in the barn.

I inspected Mom's progress with the bread; when it was done we were going for a ride in the car. Then I opened a hinged door on the right side of the kitchen where cement steps led me down into our cool root cellar.

I scrutinized shelves holding bottled fruit and pickles. Sacks of potatoes sat on the dirt floor, next to large burlap bags of wheat that Dad had taken to the mill in Logan to be ground into flour and cereal. I liked to let the coarse, ground wheat sift through my fingers. But today my hands were dirty and I was in a hurry.

One shelf held a variety of tonics like castor oil, horse lineament, paregoric, and quinine. I found a glass bottle marked "Iodine" which I grabbed then dashed back upstairs.

Mom was standing by the counter in the kitchen, gazing out the window. Helen was asleep in the bedroom.

On the counter beside Mom was a mammoth-sized McCoy mixing bowl where a thick lump of yeast was dissolving in lukewarm potato water. Eight greased bread pans were sitting on the breakfast table in the center of the room.

I sat at the breakfast table wiping dirt from my hand with a cloth, dabbing iodine over my cut.

"Do you need help with the bread?" I ventured.

Mother turned to me with a smile and tousled my hair.

"I think I can handle the bread myself. But you can bring some wood for the stove before you go back to your beets."

Dad was irrigating fields in the mid-morning sun. Troy and Mert were hoeing beets and throwing dirt clods at each other. I was supposed to join them after cleaning stalls and equipment in the barn. But I was anxious for an outing.

Our farm was three acres, with 40 more put into crop fields all around. In 1933, we did as well as anybody, selling fresh milk and eggs to the dairy, and hauling our sugar beets and grain to the mills. Whenever Dad sold a load of hay in Hyrum, he'd buy Mom a new dress at Maud's Dress Shop.

Life was beginning to look better that year. 1933 brought Roosevelt's "First Hundred Days" in office, launching public projects designed to create millions of new jobs. The future held promise.

Nibley farmers began selling more produce. Three miles north in Logan, the county seat, commerce was picking up.

Three miles south in Hyrum, on a rise overlooking the valley, Mother's hometown was growing, with shops and a high school.

Eastward in the foothills, Millville was thriving with grist mills, its rushing streams watering Nibley's farms.

Meanwhile, our beet field waited across the road. Mother often liked to watch Dad drive his team of horses down the rows, while she rocked Helen on our front porch.

"The real reason I married Leo," she'd tease, "is because he had a nice buggy with two good horses." Dad always took it as a compliment.

He worked our land using horses to pull the plows and wagons. It kept us busy. Troy, Mert, and I quickly learned the first lesson of life on a farm: the older you get, the more chores you get. We labored in the fields all day, our shirtless backs turning brown, bent over weeds and thirsty furrows.

Every morning and evening, Troy and I milked the cows. Walking out to the barn at sunrise, then again at sunset, we herded Jerseys into the stalls, then poured their frothy milk into cans for the dairy. Afterward, we fed the pigs and dozens of chickens, some roosters and turkeys, and groomed all the horses.

The dairy man came around every day to collect our milk. Troy and I had a code for him: if we put a rock next to the milk cans, he left us butter; if we put a stick instead, he left us cheese.

One morning he asked Dad why we never had any cream.

"Meb skims all the cream, so there's none to sell," Dad lamented. The truth was he didn't want to go without Mother's hot cream gravy on fried potatoes.

In those days of hard labor and little pay, Dad's reward was Mother's cooking.

Ours was rubber guns.

Every kid in Nibley knew how to make two kinds of shooters: a flipper and a rubber gun. In either case, the most crucial element was a rubber band.

A "flipper" was a sling shot, made from a Y-shaped branch of an apple tree. We cut rubber from old inner tubes of car tires; one thin slice made a round rubber band. It was natural rubber, very stretchy. Then we threaded an old shoe tongue onto the rubber band to hold a rock, and tied the rubber ends to the Y branch. A few good dirt clods and we were fully armed. Every boy in the neighborhood had a flipper in his back pocket at all times.

Troy got so good at shooting, he could knock a bird off a power line. Mother didn't like that. We had strict instructions not to sling shots at people or helpless creatures, and we were obedient.

However, the same restrictions did not apply to rubber guns.

Rubber guns shot rubber bands. You could send a zinger across the yard and hit a neighbor kid without doing serious harm.

Troy was a master rubber gun maker. He took a piece of wood lathe, 6 to 8 inches long, then put a cross piece on it for a handle and nailed a clothespin on for a trigger. Then he put a rubber band over the front end, stretched it back, and locked it into the clothespin.

When he let one fly, it could shoot 15 or 20 feet.

The down side was that if you weren't careful, the rubber band could smack you while you were loading.

One day our neighbor, Randy Sparks, tried to show off. A determined smart aleck, he was the first kid to try making a rubber rifle.

Randy showed up one day with a piece of wood lathe about three feet long. He had nailed four clothespins to one end and put four notches in the other. He was ready to show us how to shoot.

Troy stood watching him, curious. Randy had the barrel down between his legs, trying to load it. He was stretching a rubber band real tight from one end, back toward the clothespin.

Suddenly the whole thing jumped up and hit him square on the forehead. He was so stunned, he just fell over.

We all stood around him, looking at his injury. He was bleeding a little bit from a spot in the middle of his forehead, where a large goose egg was growing. Floyd ran to get Mom.

"Are ya alive or dead?" Mert chided.

Randy was too proud to cry; he shuddered, "Shut up, Mert."

Mom came out and checked Randy's head. Except for a lump, he looked normal. She washed the scrape and gave him a piece of candy. He didn't try the homemade shotgun again.

We would have sent Randy home, whimpering, but Mom was kind and gentle. Mother always wanted to make things better.

She often looked for ways to please us. When Dad sold sugar beets in Logan, she went along to buy trinkets: a bottle of finger nail polish for Barbara, or a note pad with a pencil for Helen. She took us on the train to Lagoon amusement park, where we rode the roller coaster and ate candy apples. She liked to see us happy.

One day a salesman stopped in front of our house, driving a Ford truck filled with small wicker chairs.

"Afternoon, ma'am," he greeted Mom on the front porch.

"Good day," Mother answered cheerily.

"I've got some cute chairs here for your little girls," he announced.

"Oh?" Mother said, trying not to sound too interested.

"Yep, brand new from the factory back east," he bragged. "They're surplus, so I got 'em for a special price."

Mother was curious. Barbara's birthday was July 9th and Mom wished she could get her something.

"Let me see them," Mother couldn't resist looking. She hurried down the front steps and opened the gate of our white picket fence. I followed her.

The salesman pulled out two child-sized, white wicker chairs and sat them out on the ground.

"They're adorable," Mother said, immediately charmed. I pretended to sit down in one, but she pulled me up and told me to go get Dad.

I ran to the barn where Dad was fixing a harness.

"Mama wants you," I announced.

"What for?" Dad asked.

"She wants to buy some chairs," I said.

Dad couldn't imagine, so he went to take a look. Sure enough, Mother was standing in the road looking at two little white chairs. He came up to see them for himself.

"We don't have any extra money until harvest," he reluctantly reminded her.

"I have a little money I've been saving, for rainy days," Mom suggested. When we sold milk and eggs, she kept nickels and dimes in a milk jar on the top shelf of the kitchen cupboard.

"It's up to you," Dad said.

She decided to spend her milk money on a chair for each of the girls. Barbara and Helen were delighted.

Dad kept his own stash of spare change. Harvest money barely paid the bills and bought farm supplies, so he found other ways to generate some cash. Like driving the school bus. In reality, it was a wagon with two horses; on rainy or snowy days Dad made a covered wagon and took a stove along for heat. Later, when he got a real bus, the girls used his wagon for a playhouse.

One day I asked Dad a question.

"Will you ever sell the farm and move to the city?"

"Nope," he said with certainty.

"Even if you could work in a bank and make more money?" I probed.

"Never wanted to work in a bank," he said. "I don't like staying indoors all day."

"I'd like to try working in town, after I graduate," I fantasized. "Maybe for a while."

"Suit yourself," Dad said. "It never hurts to try something different."

Meanwhile, he needed me on the farm.

Our house sat between old cottonwood shade trees with massive trunks. On the west side was a large pasture where the horses grazed near our two-story barn.

Behind our house was a wash hut and an outhouse. For seven years we had no plumbing, no running water, or indoor toilet. We pumped water from a hydrant outside, behind the house.

At sunrise, Mom would walk to the wash house and start two big boilers, then spend all day washing clothes with homemade lye soap. Doing the laundry was monumental.

Mother was a small woman, but strong. The eldest of seven girls, she always took care of others. Independent, she was never one to ask for help.

Mother carried coal and wood, pumped and hauled water, fed and clothed a family of eight, cared for my grandparents, helped all our neighbors, cooked for church parties, took meals to the elderly in Nibley, and ministered to the sick.

People used to say, "Meb, why don't you take it easy?" Her answer was always the same. "It's a privilege to do all I can."

I never heard my mother complain. Aunt Priel still insists, "I never saw such a good woman."

Personally, I could never be that good. In my view, either the kids or the chores were more than one person could handle.

One afternoon, Mom told me to round up the kids and collect their dirty clothes.

I found the boys out in the barn. Mert and Troy were scuffling on the floor, as dirty as pigs.

I grabbed them by the collar and separated them.

"I tried to make 'em stop before it started, but it didn't do no good," Floyd protested. "They were bound and determined to get into it."

"He started it," Troy said.

"No, I didn't," Mert denied.

"You both started it," I said, "and I'm ending it. Take off your clothes and get cleaned up before Mom sees you."

"I ain't got any clean clothes," Mert said.

"You can wear mine," Floyd said.

I went off to find the girls.

Helen and Barbara were playing under the big lilac tree, east of the house, near the small irrigation ditch that ran through our front yard.

Barbara was making mud pies and Helen was trying to eat one. They were both completely covered with mud. I picked up Helen before she could put her fingers into her mouth. She had mud all over her face.

I tried washing her off in the ditch. Mud was caked all over her arms and her dress. I sat her in the shallow water, since it was a hot day and the water was warm.

"Splash in the water!" Barbara said jumping in. Helen started crying and squirming to get away. I rubbed her arms in water to dissolve the mud, then washed her face, cupping my hands and pouring water over her head. By then she was screeching.

Mom came out to see what was going on. I was spattered with water and mud. Helen and Barbara were sopping wet.

"When I grow up I don't want kids," I told her. Mother smiled, picking up a soaked Helen.

"Just be like your dad and you'll turn out fine," she advised.

I left the scene to go dowse myself in the creek and float downstream for a while.

Summer offered us sensual pleasures to offset hard work. We escaped boredom and chores by playing softball in the pasture, riding horses bareback to Hyrum, and swimming in canals.

Nibley sits in an idyllic valley—600 square miles of fertile land. They call it Cache Valley, from the French word "cache" meaning "to hide." A hundred years before I was born, trappers like Jim Bridger cached fur pelts in our valley for safe keeping.

Ninety miles north of Salt Lake City, nestled between the Wellsville Mountains and the Wasatch Rockies, Cache Valley is isolated, encircled by hills. Its charming farms, willow trees and crystal streams impressed novelist Thomas Wolfe to proclaim Cache "the most lovely and enchanted valley I have ever seen."

Our preferred spot lay ten miles east of Nibley, in Blacksmith Fork Canyon where Grandpa Fred Yeates owned a few acres. In winter we sledded its snowy hills. In the summer we fished, camped, and took leisurely picnics.

Such was the case today. We were planning to take our favorite summer outing—driving our 1931 Model-A Ford. It was our first car. Dad had bought it used and he was plenty proud of it. He treated it like a baby.

The large windshield had a canvas stretched over the top, with open air at the back of the car. That's where we four boys piled inside.

Mother had never driven a car, but she wanted to learn. Every time we took it out, she asked, "Leo, can I try it?"

Dad usually just kept driving with a nervous look on his face. He was afraid to give her the wheel. So he'd answer, "How about next time, honey?"

Each time, Mom got braver and said, "Please, Leo, I really want to drive it this time."

Dad was running out of excuses, "Sweetie, next time for sure."

Next time eventually came and Dad had to let Mom drive the car. Today was finally her day.

At noon, we dropped our hoes in the field and took off running for the house.

"Mom's gonna drive!" I yelled.

Troy and Mert raced me down the row to see who would reach the car first.

"I get to sit in front!" Mert leaped over Troy.

It was a gorgeous Utah afternoon: a cobalt blue August sky with a few white clouds floating high.

Mom was already standing next to the Ford with the girls. She was wearing a pink gingham dress and a white hat. She looked like she was ready for the graduation dance.

"We've got cheese sandwiches," Barbara bragged, holding a picnic basket.

"Lemme see!" Mert grabbed the basket away as Barbara squealed. "I see bread and sweet pickles, but there ain't no cheese in here!" he cackled.

Mother checked inside. "Oh my gosh, I forgot the cheese." She was too excited about driving.

"Hey, I like pickle sandwiches," Troy teased.

"You mean knuckle sandwiches," Mert swung at the air next to his head.

"You ready, Meb?" Dad asked.

"I guess so," Mom smiled.

Mert hopped into the front seat. "It's easy, Mom, I can do it!" he pretended to steer, turning the wheel like crazy.

Dad pushed him out and got in to start up the Ford. Mom wedged her basket under the seat and the rest of us piled into the back.

Dad drove onto the dirt road in front of our house, which ran east to the Nibley corner and west toward the mountains. Our dirt road was wide, lined by occasional trees and bushes, accompanied by a large ditch that ran along the south side.

"Not many folks on this road, so I guess you can't do too much harm," Dad grinned at Mom. She laughed nervously.

He stopped the car but left it running and put on the brake. I could see a worried look on his face as he turned and announced, "Okay, Meb, it's yours."

Mom was shaking with excitement. She was breathless, completely unlike herself. I'd never seen her act that way. Mom climbed behind the wheel and took it into both hands, looking as if she'd copped a first prize at the county fair.

"Okay, honey, just hold the wheel steady and I'll handle the throttle. I'll control the speed and you steer us," Dad encouraged her cautiously.

"Okay," she smiled, anxiously.

Dad opened the throttle slowly and we started rolling. Mother gasped, nearly swooning. We were going about five miles an hour. She was holding the wheel tightly, doing fine. Until she realized she was in control of a great big machine.

She didn't know how to manage the wheel and the brakes at the same time. The car was moving faster now, ten miles per hour, and she became afraid. What if she couldn't stop?

So, she panicked.

From my vantage point in the back seat, I saw the ditch looming up like the Grand Canyon. One thrilling moment we were almost airborne, tilting like a roller coaster—then we jolted to a stop with a big thud!

We found ourselves sitting lopsided and sideways, our right front fender stuck down in the mud. There wasn't much water running in the ditch. It might have been better if there had been.

The two girls were squealing, frightened by all the excitement. We boys were cheering and laughing, "Do it again, Mom! Do it again!"

Dad looked stunned. "What happened, Meb?" was all he could say.

"I didn't know how to stop," she said. "I wanted to get off the road."

Dad just shook his head and looked down at the wheel. Then he started laughing. It didn't hurt the car much. Just a bent fender. Nobody got hurt.

We boys hopped out and helped Dad push the car out of the mud. We thought it was fun. Then we went on driving, but this time with Dad in control.

After that day, my mother never drove again. She was afraid something worse might happen the next time. Dad teased her about her driving for months.

"They have taxi drivers in Logan now," Dad would say. "Maybe we need one in Nibley …"

"I hear they drive worse than I do," Mom quipped.

"Any worse, and they'll be driving a hearse," Dad laughed.

"Go ahead and laugh," she'd say. The subject of Mother's accident was a story Dad told and retold until Mom rolled her eyes and told him to shush.

Months later, in November, there was a bad car accident up in Logan. Winter roads were slippery when the temperature dropped, and the streets in town along the foothills were very steep.

One night, a car was trying to come down the hill from the college but lost control, crashing into a deep ravine. The driver was killed.

It really shook up Mom.

She warned Dad, "Cars are dangerous. It's too easy for people to get killed."

"Don't worry," he assured her. "I won't drive up the hill when the roads are icy."

Still, the tragedy continued to bother her. It made her think about death. She was troubled by the idea that you could suddenly die one day without the chance to say goodbye. She needed some kind of reassurance.

So Dad suggested they make a pact: a promise that whoever died first— he or she—would come back to let the other one know they were okay, so to speak.

Mother liked that idea. She agreed to make the pact.

And so they did.

John Cornwell
~1996~

⁖ THREE ⁖
Easter

Utah had record rainfalls in 1937, bringing a wet, heavy winter. The next year followed with more of the same; by March 1938, it was raining or snowing every day.

Yet, Easter 1938 brought more than record-breaking snow melt.

Eight-year-old Helen was standing at the living room window, looking out at the smooth layer of wet snow that had fallen that morning. She saw something move.

"Look—a rabbit!" she called to Barbara, a year older and therefore wiser. Barbara walked over to the window and sure enough, she saw a white rabbit sitting in front of the house, by the trees.

The rabbit seemed to be watching the house—just as intently as the girls were staring at it.

"I bet it's wild. It's doesn't look like any of the neighbors' rabbits," Barbara noticed.

The rabbit stood up on two hind legs, still looking at the girls.

"He sees us!" Helen laughed.

Little Ruth ran up to the girls. "Let me see!"

Ruth was nearly five. Born in '33, she was the seventh child, a good luck charm. A little spitfire girl with long auburn hair. If Dad ever favored one child over the others, it was Ruth.

Barbara lifted Ruth up high, so she could see. The rabbit seemed transfixed on the house. It stood there staring, as if trying to say something.

"Maybe it's the Easter Bunny," teased Barbara.

Just then, Uncle Eugene's big brown car drove up with Mom and Dad inside. The rabbit disappeared.

Mom and Dad came into the house and took off their coats. They'd been up to see the doctor in Logan. I could tell by the look on their faces, it was not good news.

Mom went to her bedroom to check on baby Freddy, not quite a year old. He lay smiling in his crib, playing with a toy that Barbara made. Mother picked him up and tried to look cheerful as she carried him back into the living room.

"Mommy, Mommy," Ruth danced around her, competing for attention.

"Honey, I can't hold you right now," Mother's voice quivered.

Something was wrong. There was a heavy feeling in the air.

Mother and Dad sat down on the couch. We children found places around the room and sat quietly ... waiting for something.

"We've been to see the doctor," Dad began slowly, looking solemn. "Things don't look good." That was all he could say before his chin began to quiver.

"Are you sick, Mother?" Mert dared ask.

"The cancer has come back," Mother said, emotion in her voice.

We didn't know what to say. Her words hung in the air.

"We need to hope for the best," Dad urged, trying to sound positive, "and help Mom with her work so she won't get too tired."

It was strange to think of my mother as sick or weak. She was so full of energy, from sunrise until long after sundown. We knew she had been sick four years ago, but we thought she was well.

As children we lived in ignorant bliss. We had no clue what Mother had been going through.

❧   ❧   ❧

Cancer had first appeared in late summer of '34. Yet it had seemed more like a bad case of the flu.

Mother had first noticed it one day when she was canning peaches. She'd been lifting the steamer on and off the stove, filled with quart jars of fruit. Each jar was packed with fresh peaches and syrup, so the steamer was heavy.

Every time she lifted, she noticed a pain in her left arm. Finally, she reached up to feel under her arm and rub it a little. When she touched the sore spot, she felt a couple of small lumps. They were hard, about the size of grapes. They hurt. She had an uneasy feeling about them that made her worry the rest of the day.

That night she told Dad, "Honey, feel these lumps under my arm." As he pressed them with his fingers, she winced in pain. "Ouch! That hurts."

"Those knots are kinda big," he was concerned. "You better go see the doctor and have it checked out."

"What do you think?" she asked him.

"I don't know. But lumps need to come out," he guessed.

The next day, she rode the train to the doctor's office in Logan. Dr. Burgess looked at Mother's arm and told her the lumps needed to be removed. He suspected that they were cancer.

When he said it, the word sent fear through her like a shiver. "Cancer" was a cold-sounding word.

A few days later Dr. Burgess had performed the surgery. He removed four hard lumps from underneath her left arm. Grandma Shaw went to stay with Mom while they kept her in the hospital for a week.

For two months, Mother went back to the doctor for treatments. And she prayed fervently every day that she would be healed.

Then Mother suddenly got better. She seemed healed by faith and the grace of God. So she went back to doing her usual things. Cooking and washing, feeding nine people, and keeping house.

Three years later Mother was happy when little Freddy was born. Like the infant economy, baby Fred was a new beginning. Mother outdid herself taking care to see everything was just right. She was busier than ever, making plans.

☘   ☘   ☘

I wish I could say the cancer had gone away. Unfortunately, it was lying dormant. By Easter 1938, my mother was ill.

For several weeks that spring, she experienced pain and weakness in her left arm. When it began to really bother her, she rubbed it and probed underneath.

Sure enough, three new lumps had formed, hard like before. Her old scars ached and her left arm felt weaker than her right.

Spring was just around the corner, like this year's plans. But spring had brought my mother a turn for the worse.

Mom sat on the couch holding baby Fred, singing a song for Ruth. Dad walked outside, talking to Uncle Eugene.

"The doctor says he'll need to operate as soon as possible," Dad confided.

"Let me know if you need money," Gene offered. He was Dad's best friend.

"Thanks, Gene," Dad answered.

Dad and Mom made plans for her to have another surgery. She rode the train up to Logan twice to let the doctor run some tests.

There was a lot to do. Six of us were in school, with eight children in the house between the ages of one and seventeen.

Grandpa Shaw told Dad, "Leo, you've gotta get some running water into this house."

"I know," Dad agreed. "Can you help me?"

So they spent two days installing pipes to bring running water from the hydrant into our kitchen. When they finished, Mert kept turning on the water in the sink, just to see it run.

One week after Mom got the news from Dr. Burgess, he scheduled her surgery at Logan Hospital. Dad and Grandma Shaw took Mother to Logan in Aunt Reva's car; our Model-A had given out the year before. Dad stayed with Mom.

Aunt Priel came to stay with us while Mom was away. Full of energy and funny stories, Priel was the best thing next to Mom. She baked us cookies and played games.

Two nights later Dad called to say that Mother was sleeping and he would be home. We sat in the living room and waited.

When Dad came in the door, the moment he saw us he started to weep. It was the first time I ever saw my father cry.

"It was bad," he confessed, hugging Priel. "The cancer was spread all over her left side."

He sat down on the couch and began describing it all without realizing we didn't fully understand.

"They had to remove her breast," he announced, "and everything around it."

This really startled us. We didn't know what to think.

"The cancer was advanced, in her lymph glands," he went on. "The doctor tried to remove it all. He cut away everything he could see—he even took the muscle from her arm."

It was shocking to imagine these things happening to our Mother's body.

Then my father just broke down and bawled, right out loud. He shuddered, his face pressed into his hands.

We boys started crying just because Dad was; the girls were crying, frightened by all the drama.

Meanwhile at the hospital, Mother was trying to recover. Grandma Shaw was there, but she had gone to pieces. She just couldn't believe it.

How could cancer strike someone as good as her daughter? And why at Easter of all times?

I'll never forget how strange Mother looked the day she came home. She was gaunt and weak, all bandaged on the left side, her face as white as a sheet. Dad put her into bed, where she rested for three weeks.

Grandma Shaw and Priel took turns staying with us, while Mother was sick in bed. Slowly, Mom began to regain her strength.

After a few weeks, she was up and walking. She had to go back to the hospital for treatments which were supposed to help, but they made her sick. After each treatment, she had to rest for a couple of days. Whenever she regained her energy, she'd go back for another treatment.

Somehow, Mother kept going; when she wasn't resting, or working, she was singing or praying. She wanted to resume her routine.

Mom was not the same after her surgery, but she didn't seem to notice; or maybe we didn't seem to notice. She did her usual things and acted normal. I think she hid suffering from herself.

It should have seemed odd, but Mother never really talked about the cancer. She just wanted it to go away.

However, we soon realized that cancer was a visitor we couldn't ignore.

One morning a few months later, Mom was in the kitchen making breakfast. I came out of the barn after milking cows. Just then, a hobo came walking into the yard. A stranger, from the freight train passing by.

We lived just a few yards from the tracks. Two railroad lines crossed the county, like long black scars stitched across a patchwork quilt of green and brown fields. One line was a passenger train to Salt Lake that we had to board in Logan.

The other line was a local train from Cache Junction. Its single set of tracks ran just west of our house, so close, you could feel the ground vibrate whenever it passed by. The local train carried grain and beets, and had one passenger car. It came by once a day and would take you to Logan for 15 cents.

With the freight tracks so close, a lot of hobos walked by our house. Mom usually gave them something to eat. Bread and cheese, or whatever she had on hand. The word got out and hobos often came knocking on our back door.

Today, I thought I'd intercept and fetch some bread and butter from the kitchen. I knew Mother wasn't feeling well.

"Howdy," the stranger said as he walked up.

"Hi," I answered. "Where are you headed?"

"Salt Lake. After that, who knows?" he smiled. He was very thin. Looked like he could use some food.

"Would you like some bread and milk?" I offered.

"I sure could use some," he grinned.

"Let me grab some for you. Be right back," I promised.

I went into the kitchen. Mother was stirring gravy on the stove while Barbara played with Freddy.

"Mom, there's a hobo outside; how about I give him some bread and jam?" I asked.

Mother turned to smile at me. She liked to feed the hobos because they really needed a meal.

"Let him come in," she said. This was odd. She usually handed them food at the door. I watched her leave the stove and go to the back door. "Would you like some biscuits and gravy?" she asked the stranger.

That hobo looked like someone had just given him a hundred dollars. "Boy, I sure would!" he responded. "Thank you, ma'am."

He came in and Mom sat him down at the breakfast table.

"What's your name?" I asked him.

"Harley," he said.

Mother laid two open-faced biscuits on his plate, then ladled steaming hot gravy over them. No one made gravy like hers, swimming with sausage, cream, butter, salt and pepper.

"You eat up," she smiled. He took a large mouthful and closed his eyes as he tasted it.

"Mmmmm boy ... that's good gravy," he managed to say between mouthfuls. "Best biscuits I ever tasted, ma'am."

I watched him spoon up every last bite on the plate. Then he sat back and sighed, rubbing his ribs.

"I believe I can die happy now, ma'am," Harley grinned.

"What do you mean, talking like that?" Mom laughed. "My biscuits and gravy ought to keep you alive for awhile."

"Your biscuits and gravy could heal the sick and cure the dying," he returned.

"I guess we'll see," Mom suddenly grew quiet.

Harley got up to leave. "Thank you, ma'am. You're an angel of mercy. If I see anyone who looks to be ailing, I'll send 'em your way." She smiled wistfully.

Harley walked back toward the train racks. I had more chores waiting for me in the barn.

"Helen, can you help me clean up the dishes?" Mother called. Barbara was holding Freddy. All of a sudden Mother swooned, losing her balance as she leaned over the sink. She caught herself, but her knees buckled and she slowly sank down, her knees hitting the floor.

"Mom!" I rushed over to help her. She was white and pasty looking like she was going to faint.

"Help me get to the couch so I can rest," she said.

I helped her into the living room.

"Mom, are you okay?" Barbara asked. We crowded around her, afraid she would pass out.

"I'm fine," she said. "I'm just tired. A little nap and I'll be okay."

We covered her with a yellow afghan that she had crocheted and tucked it in around her sides. It was obvious Mom was not okay. She was sick. This was something that biscuits and gravy would not help. It was something we didn't know how to fix. We didn't know what to do.

Suddenly the life we had known was fading. We were in unfamiliar territory and it was a frightening place. The person whom we depended on, was changing into someone we didn't know. Something was taking her away.

Cancer came to our family like a thief. Unlike the harmless hobos who came looking for food, cancer was a cruel stranger—a malignant criminal. Out of nowhere it appeared one day and robbed us, of innocence. And then it tried to take away our happiness.

∾ FOUR ∾
November

W e boys were sitting at the dining table, listening to the radio. The static noise on our Philco came in so loud it could knock your ears off. We turned the knob constantly, trying to tune it.

Shows aired on the radio every evening around supper time. We heard "Amos and Andy," the "Lone Ranger," and the "Charlie McCarthy Show." Charlie was Edgar Bergen's dummy, who made funny jokes and puns. Edgar had another dummy named Mortimer Snerd, the country bumpkin. Of course, Edgar did all three voices.

Mert went around the house imitating Charlie and Mortimer until we made him quit. He was a teenager now, at 14; Troy was two years older than Mert, and I was 17.

Troy, Mert, and I liked listening to sports, especially baseball. We had to know who won each game. Troy and I rooted for the New York Yankees and Babe Ruth. Mert chose the Brooklyn Dodgers just to be different. Dad liked the Baltimore Orioles and Chicago Whitesox.

We faithfully listened to the radio show about "Jack Armstrong—The Aaaaaall American Boy!" Jack was a national symbol of athletic achievement for high school boys like us. Mainly, he made everyone want to buy Wheaties, since his picture was on the box.

Today's story was about Jack and his athletic prowess in football. Jack's voice came on, saying, "It's great playing football! Today I'm gonna score a touchdown!" Then the commentator gave us a play-by-play account. You could hear Jack kick that ball and the crowd cheer. Jack Armstrong was amazing. He could do anything, play every sport—all because he ate Wheaties.

The girls usually listened to music in the afternoon. By the late '30s, popular music was moving from the "flapper era" into swing band and big band sounds. We listened to Paul Whiteman or the Kay Kyser orchestra and his "college of musical knowledge."

The new band music caused a dance craze in the late '30s, so Arthur Murray began advertising that he could teach anyone to dance.

Aunt Reva and Aunt Marvel wanted to learn. They sent for some Arthur Murray dancing instructions advertised on the radio. A few weeks later, they received in the mail a set of black footstep prints, that would stick to the floor. Numbered 1, 2, 3, 4, each black footprint showed Reva and Marvel where to put their feet, in order to dance correctly.

Barbara, Helen, and Floyd watched them practice dancing, while trying not to laugh out loud as Reva and Marvel followed the steps. Later Floyd and Barbara would hop around our living room, mimicking the Murray motto: "Arthur Murray taught me dancing in a hurry."

Radio was our window to the world. We believed everything we heard.

I remember Sunday night before Halloween 1938, when the Columbia Broadcasting Network aired "The War of the Worlds." A reporter alarmed us listeners with his eyewitness account of a live invasion. We thought it must be the Germans, because they had rockets; they were launching a worldwide war! The show terrified not only our neighborhood but the entire nation; folks were calling each other on the phone all night to find out if it was true.

It was only a radio drama. Real life would soon be bad enough.

By November, Mom was really sick. She was losing weight and growing weaker. From time to time, she rode the train to Logan for treatments.

The pain in her left arm was growing much worse. The doctor had removed so much flesh, her arm ached a great deal. She was having difficulty lifting or moving it.

I helped Mom with cooking before and after school. Barbara, age 9, and Helen, age 8, helped with some household chores. Aunt Reva and Marvel came by to give her a hand.

Mama loved to cuddle little Freddy, but he was getting too heavy and squirmed to get down and explore. Barbara was watching him most of the time. Mother had to rest often on her bed. She used the time to read stories to five-year-old Ruth.

One morning after Dad left the house, I went looking for Mom in the kitchen. She was sitting down at the breakfast table, looking awfully tired.

"How are you feeling, Mother?" I asked.

"I believe I'm getting a little better," she offered.

One could see she wasn't. She was getting worse. Still, she was positive.

"I plan to be baking pies when I'm ninety years old," she smiled at me.

"And I plan to be eating them," I smiled back.

For the most part, we were unaware of how bad Mother was feeling. Seven kids were running around the house as usual, hungry, noisy, or arguing.

We listened to radio news about gangsters back east, and played cops and robbers, always letting the cops win. In real life, mobsters were losing power after Roosevelt ended prohibition. We were captivated by news of John Dillinger betrayed by "the lady in red" who accompanied him to the movies; as they came out of the theater, "G-men" waited to shoot Dillinger down. Pretty Boy Floyd,

Baby Face Nelson, and Bonnie & Clyde would also face the government men, forerunners of the FBI.

We boys loved going to the movies to see Tom Mix, Hopalong Cassidy, and Erroll Flynn. Any time we could break away from chores, we'd ride the train to Logan. Admission to a movie at the Roxy Theatre was 10 cents. We could lose ourselves in action pictures on the big screen.

In November, everyone was going to see "Heart of the North" about the Canadian mounted police. Cousin Budge always said, "People should have better things to do than go watch some pictures on a screen." In a few months, record numbers of movie goers would flock to see "Gone with the Wind" and "The Wizard of Oz."

Meanwhile, Dad was worried about Mom. She was failing noticeably and needed help. He asked Reva and Marvel if they could help fix meals.

Mother also needed medical attention yet Dad still had her surgery to pay off. All he could do was try to keep everything going—the farm and taking care of Mom.

He began working at the post office early this year, in November. The extra money wasn't for Christmas; we needed it for medical bills.

"How are things going?" Eugene asked as they sorted mail.

"Meb's getting a lot worse," Dad confided. "I don't know how long she can keep going."

"What's the doctor's prediction?" Gene inquired.

"She could go another couple of months or a few weeks. It's hard to know with cancer," Dad answered.

"Who will take care of the kids?" Gene wondered.

"I don't know," Dad said. "I worry about it. The boys can fend for themselves, with school and chores. The girls still need mothering. Ruth is only five."

"What about Freddy?" Eugene asked.

"Freddy needs his mom ..." Dad's voice quivered.

Uncle Eugene couldn't think of anything to say. They worked in silence. Constant work kept Dad from caving in to fear and emotion.

Meanwhile, life went on around us, unaware that our way of life was ending. The world was changing in 1938.

Our economy was showing vital signs of recuperation from the Depression. The initial "recovery" had lasted through 1936, then ebbed back into recession; but 1938 saw a steady rise in business and the end of economic decline. Lifted by the spirit of recovery, families were looking forward to the future.

There were other signs of the changing times. By fall 1938, all the streetcars in Salt Lake City ceased running, because automobile manufacturers had lobbied to end them. By 1940, motorized buses replaced electric trolley cars.

Although recovery was under way, what really ended the Depression was World War II. Eugene was right; nothing but war could finally cure it. The threat of war got business going strong, producing supplies. By 1940, industry boomed, ending unemployment.

During 1938, everyone was expecting war—Hitler seemed unstoppable. World War I was still vivid in everyone's memory, so the specter of another war kept people glued to the radio for news of Europe and broadcasts of Hitler's speeches. 1938 was an ominous window of time, when life was full of promise and the world still out of balance. Times were tense with ghosts of poverty and war, fear and hope.

Meanwhile, in Utah the rains kept coming; by November 1938, they totalled 18 inches. Even the weather was foreboding bad times.

In Utah, we have amazing storms: thunder and rain storms, hail and lightning shows, and wicked winter blizzards. Here, the land and weather are extreme, every season intense. We can be smothered in snow, or hidden under blustery thunderheads, bathed in crisp vistas of breezy clouds and mountains, or bleached by a blazing summer heat.

Storms leave California in a hurry and rush across the deserts of Nevada; upon reaching Salt Lake, they collide with the Rocky Mountains on the lower slopes of the Wasatch Front, in our front yards. We live in a swath of fertile land where mountains meet sky and abruptly drop down into rolling foothills.

Here a thunderstorm can sound like an earthquake. Cold air from the north meets our southwestern desert winds and whips up a frenzy, especially in November. If the temperature drops below freezing, the sky can dump a ton of wet snow within hours. If the temperature stays warmer, gale force winds and rain can ravage trees and yards. This was the case one day in November 1938. The day Mother prayed for help.

That morning when we got up, the sky was gray and brooding. Dad left after breakfast to work at the post office. Troy and I went out to milk cows and feed the animals.

The wind began to whine around us, stirring up clouds, thicker and darker. As we finished milking, dense black clouds were moving downward like enormous dark forces, bunching up, gathering intensity.

"It's gonna be a bad one!" Troy yelled as we closed the barn door. The wind was fighting us, trying to pull the door from our grasp.

"Better let Snip loose," I yelled back. Three of our horses were already out in the pasture, whinnying to Snip who waited in the corral.

Snip was anxious, pacing inside the fence. I put a rope around her neck and led her out the gate as Troy held it open. Just then a roll of thunder grumbled up, sounding like the earth had a hungry stomach. Snip spooked and jumped sideways, pulling the rope out of my hands.

I scrambled to grab the rope then ran toward the pasture, pulling Snip behind me. Troy lowered the top pole of the fence and I coaxed her over. Slipping out of her rope, she took off running with the other horses, kicking her hind legs as Troy and I put the fence back into place.

A huge streak of lightning cracked across the sky with electric tentacles: a signal for the storm to release its burden. Thunder struck sounding like god's fury. Hailstones started flying.

"Those things hurt!" Troy laughed as we ran for the door. Ice balls the size of marbles were pelting us. They sprayed all over the floor when we burst into the kitchen.

"It's coming down hard, Mom!" Troy warned, breathless. Mother was trying to feed Freddy, but he was fussing, frightened by the sounds of the storm.

Troy and I watched out the window as heavy black clouds began pressing down on the hills around us. Lightning was coming down fierce and low enough to strike a farm up on the ridge.

It flashed into trees on the hillside.

"Holy cow! Did you see that?" Troy called. "Those trees are smoking!"

I could see gray wisps rising from the treetops. Mert was excited. "I want to go get a better look!" He was curious enough to head outside in that direction.

"Oh no you don't!" I grabbed him before he could get to the door. "We don't want your skinny body smoking in the yard!"

Troy and Barbara laughed. Ruth and Helen couldn't see the humor and grabbed onto Mert's legs so he couldn't walk outside. He went walking around the living room with them hanging onto him, saying "I'm lightning! I'm the lightning man!"

Another streak of fluorescent white crackled about two miles away, across the fields. A moment later a huge thunderclap resounded, with enough force to scare Mert. He and the girls jumped onto the couch with Barbara. Troy and I were still posted at the windows.

Troy gasped. "That lightning just struck a haystack! It's burning!"

"Maybe the rain will put it out," I ventured, hoping for the best. There was no way anyone could stop a fire in a lightning storm—it was too dangerous. I stood at the window and watched the haystack burn.

"Mom, will it strike our house?" Helen cried.

"No, it would hit the barn first," I tried to comfort her. "The barn is higher and has a weather vane on top." I was still worried. I didn't want the barn to catch fire.

The storm was rolling in tighter, getting darker outside. Thunderclaps drowned out all other sounds, closing in around us, sounding like the earth was breaking wide open. As I said, we have some incredible storms in Cache Valley. This was the worst I'd ever seen.

Two haystacks on the hill lit up like kindling sticks. To us it looked as if Hyrum was on fire.

"All of you stay in here and keep still. I'm going into the bedroom by myself," Mother said, anxiously. "Keith and Troy, you watch everyone and keep them calm."

Mom was unnerved by the storm. She didn't like being on the farm in this weather. Without Dad around, she was afraid.

Barely able to lift Freddy, she carried him to her bedroom and put him on the bed. She wanted to be alone so she could pray. Mother was always praying, on her knees.

Fear had taken hold of her. She was losing composure, shaking like a leaf. There was no place to go, nowhere to turn, but to God.

Freddy was crying, frightened by the storm. Mother felt weak and frail. She knelt down by him on her bed, leaning her upper body across the mattress, resting her head in her hands.

"Dear God, you've helped me so many times. Please, Father, help me now." She felt desperate. "Please protect us. Don't let the storm harm us," she pleaded.

She paused and rocked Freddy on the bed, silently asking God to help him sleep.

Then she collapsed into deeper emotions and fear, crying, "Please, God, please help me. Help me be strong."

She began questioning, "Why ... why am I dying? What did I do wrong?" She didn't understand it.

Had she inherited cancer from an ancestor, like her gift of cooking? Was she causing it somehow, like giving yourself a nervous stomach? Had she been working too hard?

She had always been so strong and happy. Why was her body quitting when she didn't want to quit?

"Please, God, let me live. Please help me get better," she begged.

"Why is mama in there?" Ruth asked Barbara. The three girls were huddled together on the big rag rug in front of the couch.

"Hush, she'll be back in a few minutes," Barbara held Ruth close to her.

Troy had a plan, "Let's watch the lightning strike, then count the seconds 'til the thunder."

A huge streak lit up the sky. "Whoa!" everybody shrieked at once. Blue and green light played in the clouds.

Troy counted, "One one thousand, two one thousand, three one thou—"

C r a c k! Lightning echoed in a deafening thunderbolt and everybody jumped for the floor.

"Why does it do that?" Helen asked, frightened.

"Keith, do you know?" Barbara asked, trembling.

"Lighting moves faster than thunder," I offered. "You can see lightning strike, but it takes the sound a few seconds to get here."

"Really?" Helen had a look of disbelief on her face.

"Yep, it's true," Troy confirmed. "We learned it in school."

All of a sudden, cold rain started coming down in big heavy drops, mixed with hail. It rained so hard it sounded like someone was throwing rocks onto the roof. The cloud color changed to a purplish-pink hue.

Mert started singing, "It's raining, it's pouring, the old man is snoring!"

Mother had been in the bedroom for quite awhile. I thought I'd better check to see if she was all right. I tiptoed to her door.

In her room, Mother was still kneeling, waiting for some answer or feeling of comfort. She let her mind flow free, open to any impression that might come.

A quiet stillness answered. She felt calm.

Freddy was fast asleep on the bed. She put pillows on both sides of him and left him there. She didn't feel like lifting him or disturbing his sleep.

Mother came out of her room, looking more peaceful. She glanced outside to see if the storm had slowed any, but it was still going full force. Thunder and lightning were flashing inside pastel colored clouds; rain and hail were pelting the valley.

"Winter's here," she said matter-of-factly. "Looks like a hard winter ahead."

Mother sat in the rocking chair and Ruth climbed up into her lap. With her good arm around Ruth, she let her sore arm rest.

Ruth asked, "Mommy, why does your arm hurt?"

Mother tried to smile, but pain welled up in her eyes.

"I don't know, honey. Maybe you can ask God to make it better." A few tears ran down her face like rain streaking the window panes.

"Her arm hurts 'cause the doctor cut it," Mert announced, a tinge of anger in his voice.

Mert and Mom were opposites; what she wouldn't say, he did. Mom put things nicely, while Mert blurted out the truth. I often thought that between the two of them, you got the whole picture.

Yet Mother didn't have any answers. She didn't know why she was dying. She guessed maybe we aren't meant to know.

Like a storm on the horizon moving with forces beyond our control, my mother's cancer had returned with a fury. It descended upon us as abruptly as winter had announced itself in cold rains coming from the north.

∽ FIVE ∽
December

December arrived looking dreary. Wet, but not freezing cold, it rained constantly in the valleys, while the mountains brushed snow from low skies.

In our home, life took a drastic turn for the worse.

It was clear that Mother was not expected to live. Dad told us the terrible news one evening while Mom was resting in bed.

We were sitting in the dining room after dinner, listening to the radio.

"I've been talking to the doctor," Dad began, proceeding carefully. "He says we should prepare for the worst."

"What do you mean, Dad?" I ventured.

He could think of no other way to say it.

"The doctor says Mother is going to die." I wished he could soften the blow.

Nobody said anything. The radio program went on, sounding utterly ridiculous.

"When, Dad?" I finally asked, for lack of anything else to say. "When will she die?"

"We don't know. She may not make it through Christmas," he warned.

"Why can't she get better?" Troy wondered.

"She's too sick," Dad's chin quivered, melting the corners of his eyes. "But I know Meb; she'll hang on as long as she can."

We sat stunned, saying nothing, because there was nothing to say. His words held finality, suspended forever in the air.

We had been told the truth, unsure how to comprehend it. Over the following weeks, we dealt with it in different ways.

Dad tried to stall the inevitable by keeping busy. I went about quietly, withdrawn, wondering how things would proceed.

Troy and Mert avoided the issue completely, staying outside most of the time.

Floyd and Barbara didn't comprehend death: Floyd didn't believe she would die, and Barbara kept asking when Mother would get better.

Helen and Ruth were simply too young to understand what was happening.

Mother herself didn't want to believe she was dying. She was still trying to be normal. She kept moving through her daily tasks, slowly, resisting the cancer as much as she could.

I kept an eye on her, in case she might falter, I told myself. In reality, I needed to be near her. I tended to check on her often, standing by her doorway to see how she was doing.

One day I heard her talking to Grandma Shaw in the bedroom.

"The doctors can't do anything for me," she admitted. "But I know that if God wills it, he can heal me. Because I've been healed before."

Grandma was treating Mother with a poultice that was supposed to draw out the cancer. Grandma believed in home remedies and the power of prayer.

"I've seen miracles happen," Grandma agreed. "If anyone deserves a miracle, it's you, Meb."

"If it's not the will of God that I live, then I guess I will die," Mother conceded. "But I would like to live and care for my children."

Grandma didn't say anything more.

Meanwhile Christmas was coming. Holiday decorations were appearing on the streets in Logan. We wanted to drive to town and see the lights, but we didn't have a car.

"Dad, can we go see the Christmas lights?" Barbara tugged.

"We don't have a car, honey," he answered.

"Please, Daddy," Floyd and Helen chimed.

"Maybe cousin Blanche will give us a ride," Dad suggested.

"Call her!" the children insisted.

Budge had a brand new car. He was successful, likely because he didn't mind telling people that he gave the best haircut in town for the best price. He and Blanche had means, but only one child to spend it on. Blanche had a daughter Barbara's age named Pat, but she longed for another child. They loved the energy of us eight kids. Budge wrestled with Troy and Mert, while Blanche cuddled Freddy so much she nearly kissed him blue.

Blanche was unable to have more children. I overheard her talking to Mother about it one day.

"It seems so unfair," Mother said, while peeling potatoes in the kitchen. "I get pregnant every year or two without even trying. Yet for some reason, you can't at all."

"You never know what life has in store," Blanche answered. "Of all the things that could go wrong, I never dreamed I wouldn't be able to have more children."

Blanche and Mother were about the same age. When they were young, they played together and went to the same school. After they married they remained close friends.

When the cancer returned, Mother confided to Blanche about it.

"I just can't believe it's back," Mom said. "I never dreamed I'd get cancer."

"You don't seem sick," Blanche offered. "You look perfectly healthy."

"If I have to die of cancer, I just want to live ten years longer—until my children are older," she said optimistically.

Blanche just nodded.

Today would be a good day for mother to see Blanche. Dad decided to call Blanche for a ride.

We were without a car and broke. We didn't have any cash after paying the doctor bills. Even with Dad working at the post office, there was little money.

Troy and I worked odd jobs, while Mert and Floyd were handling more of the chores around the farm. Aunt Priel and Grandma Shaw were helping Mom with Freddy and the house.

Money or not, Dad knew we all needed a break; an outing was long overdue and would boost our spirits.

"Blanche?" Dad asked when she picked up the phone.

"These kids are driving me crazy, begging to see the lights in town. Do you and Budge have any time this week to go with us?"

Blanche was always in the mood to see us kids.

"Tonight? Are you sure?" Dad asked. He had a hard time hearing her voice in the phone, with Barbara and Floyd whooping it up in the background.

"That would be wonderful. We'll be ready at six." He hung up the phone. He knew it would cheer Mother to go for a drive.

Two hours later, we were all in Budge's car, three adults with a baby in front, seven kids squeezed in the back seat. We drove up the road to Logan, passing a machine shop and a filling station. I always liked driving to town; it gave me a feeling that life or destiny held something more in the future.

As we entered town along Main Street, exuberant holiday symbols greeted us. However, this year the big red bells and candy canes seemed to lack their usual charm.

The Bamberger street car was running, clanging to announce its arrival at the corner of First and Main Streets. Clarion bells in the university's Old Main tower chimed Christmas carols. Shoppers scurried along the sidewalks.

"Let's go to the Bluebird," Budge announced. "Our treat."

Now that cheered us.

In the middle of Main Street was the Bluebird Cafe, "Famous for Fine Chocolates and Ice Cream Since 1914." The Bluebird had charming window displays; today, a nativity scene lured shoppers to stop and buy sweets.

We piled out of Budge's car, into the restaurant. Blanche had been shopping with her daughter Pat and they were waiting there to meet us.

The dining room held large round tables and a soda fountain along the wall with a row of shiny black stools. Glass shelves displayed homemade pies, tall soda glasses and fancy dishes for ice cream. A grand staircase led upstairs to a second floor ballroom where they held parties and dances.

Troy, Mert, Floyd, and I grabbed a stool at the fountain, but Dad wanted us to sit together at a table. The adults sat with Helen and Pat; Blanche was holding Freddy and Dad was holding Ruth. We five siblings sat at the next table.

"I'll have hot apple pie with ice cream," Budge ordered. Dad wanted the same.

Blanche said, "I'll take a warm piece of blackberry pie."

Mother just wanted hot cider.

"We'll each have a vanilla and strawberry ice cream sundae with chocolate topping," I ordered for us five. We didn't care if it was cold outside. Ice cream was heaven.

At a table next to us, two teenaged girls were wearing new striped dresses and felt hats. Their hair was perfectly curled and they were sitting on cashmere coats.

"We're getting a piano for Christmas," a blonde girl was saying, as she spooned strawberry topping.

"I'm glad we're not," Mert shot back. "I hate piano lessons." The girl gave him a dirty look.

"Are we getting anything this year?" Helen asked me.

"New clothes," I guessed Grandma and Aunt Priel would sew us something.

When the sundaes came, Troy stopped talking about wooden airplanes long enough to eat a mouthful of chocolate. Mert was chewing peanuts and opened up wide so the girls at the next table could see.

Budge was telling Dad about the new 1939 Fords. I sure wished we could get a car.

Mother was enjoying herself, perking up in the restaurant. She told a funny story about Ruth, who had tried to get paper dolls out of a sack and turned it upside down to look inside. To her surprise, the dolls and all their clothes had fluttered out over her like snow flakes.

Everybody looked at Ruth and laughed. She just shrugged her shoulders and scrunched her little face.

As we finished our ice cream I could see Mother starting to tire. Dad noticed it too.

"I guess we should be leaving," he said. "Got a lot to do at home."

Dad helped Mother get up, but she faltered and had to sit back down. Everyone wondered if she was alright.

"Too much apple cider," she joked. Blanche laughed politely.

The next day Mom stayed in bed until late in the morning. Our jaunt to Logan had taken more energy than she let on.

Mother kept struggling to do normal tasks, while growing weaker by the day. I noticed she didn't have much appetite and was losing weight. She had to rest in bed for several hours, daily.

"I don't want to be bedridden, Leo," she told Dad. "I want to keep going as long as I can."

"I know, Meb," Dad consoled.

She couldn't understand why she was dying.

Something in her body wanted to die, or believed it couldn't live. For some reason she couldn't keep doing what she normally did—moving, working, mothering. Why was her body giving up?

Whatever the cause, she couldn't keep going. Her body was shutting down. She dreaded losing her mobility.

I wished there was something I could do.

That day I got an idea.

The previous summer I had worked in Nevada on our cousin's farm, hauling hay and driving horses. They had paid me ten dollars a week.

I had come back home with $160 for my future. After buying new shoes for us boys, I had put the rest away.

Now I thought of a better use for that money. I would give fifty dollars to Dad, to help pay for Mother's medical bills.

With the rest, I would buy a gift.

I went to my room and pulled a cigar box from under the floorboard. Although President Roosevelt had come on the radio telling us to put our money in the bank, I wanted to keep mine safe at home. Inside the box were three fifty-dollar bills and some change. I took out two and put them in a small leather wallet that Troy had made for me.

Troy was out in the barn fiddling with some old bicycle tires and wood planks.

"What are you doing?" I asked.

"I was thinking maybe I could make a go cart," Troy said.

"Let's go up to Logan and do some shopping," I said. He looked at me like I was crazy.

"Okay," he agreed.

Troy and I walked to the railroad tracks and hopped the train to Logan. We got off and walked a few blocks to Main Street where a car lot was selling brand new cars. We stopped to look at each one, running our fingers along the curved fenders, painted shiny black, dark brown or light tan.

The only car we'd ever had was our Model A.

They had some nice used cars, too. I looked at a black 1938 Plymouth. The little sign in the windshield said $300.

Then the owner walked up. "How you boys doin' today?" he ventured, assuming we were daydreaming.

"Pretty good." I answered. "We're looking for a car."

"Really?" he said, surprised. "Well, this Plymouth is a beaut. It's barely a year old and runs like a dream."

"Would you take $150 down, with payments on the balance?" I blurted out suddenly. All I had to spend was $100 but I hoped I could borrow $50 from someone.

"My mom is real sick with cancer and I'd like to buy it for her," I explained.

He scratched his chin, looking at the car, and then at me, then back at the car again.

Finally he said, "Son, I believe I could let you take this car for a down payment of $100. That is, if you have cash today. And, if you sign a loan agreement with me for the balance." He smiled at me with a deep look in his eyes.

"Sold!" I yelped, grabbing his hand and shaking it. I was so excited I could hardly stand still. I pulled out my wallet and handed him my two fifty-dollar bills. "Thank you so much, sir!

"I believe you'll like this car," he smiled. "Just tell your mama I hope she gets better."

A half hour later, I was driving a shiny black Plymouth down Main Street, heading south for the country road to Nibley. That road to town had kept its promise of better things. I was in a daze. I couldn't believe I was buying this car, or even driving it for that matter. I drove slowly; rain was making the road a bit slippery.

I thought about how surprised Mom and Dad would be. Life was so grim these days, I really wanted to cheer them up. This car would do it.

"I just wish I could ease her suffering," I said out loud to Troy.

"Huh?" Troy was lost in his own dream world.

"Mother. I wish I could make things easier for her," I said.

"This car ought to lift her spirits," Troy answered. "Just wait 'til everyone sees it!" He was already driving it in his mind.

John Cornwell
~1996~

～ SIX ～
Trees

ur new car bolstered everyone's spirits. Oddly enough, it even helped to prolong my mother's life.

Mother was becoming riddled with cancer. Her petite body was retaining water, holding so much fluid it bloated her. The inflammation accumulated until she was so swollen, she could barely move. Her pain was excruciating.

Doctor Burgess told Dad that Mother would have to be "tapped."

"Tapped?" Dad asked, concerned.

"To drain her body of excess fluid," the doctor answered.

"It sounds like what you do to a tree," Dad protested, dreading to hear more.

"Actually, it's a similar process," the doctor responded. "We insert a needle and tube, then drain the liquid."

"And if she doesn't have the tapping done?" Dad was curious.

"Leo, if she doesn't have the fluids tapped, she'll die—in a matter of days," Dr. Burgess warned.

Dad just sat looking at the doctor, and cried.

"Alright," Dad said, wiping his face.

"I'll need to do it here, at the hospital. You'll have to bring her up to Logan," the doctor explained.

"Well, we have a car now," Dad informed him, "but she's awfully inflamed, so it's painful for her to move around."

"I know," Dr. Burgess said sympathetically. "We can give her shots for the pain."

So Mother went to be tapped. It became a torturous ritual.

She waited until she felt the most extreme discomfort and distress. I can still see her lying in bed, trying not to move.

When she reached a point where she couldn't stand it any longer, she would go to the hospital.

We had to lift her out of bed to put her into the car. It hurt her to move because she was so swollen; inflammation has a way of screaming at you. Troy and I carried her, while she held her breath.

Once we got her in the front seat of the Plymouth, she just sat there gasping, all the way to Logan. Then we had to hurt her again by getting her out of the car and carrying her into the hospital.

At the hospital they tapped her. As the doctor had said, it was like tapping a tree and letting the liquid out.

Fluid became trapped in her stomach and chest, even in the lining of her lungs. It could drown her, so they went in with a probe to drain the excess water. They gave her a shot first, to help deaden the pain.

As she laid on the bed, they inserted a long needle into her chest area and stomach where she was swollen. Then they attached tubes that drew the fluid out. She was so inflamed, it burned her skin to insert the drains. She cried out every time they did it.

Actually, the tapping helped. The pressure in her body was so acute, its bizarre and painful release was a relief by comparison.

This ritual was cruel and kind, causing pain, yet bringing temporary relief. It was an ordeal for her to endure, and for us to witness.

Grandma Shaw rode the train to be with Mother at the hospital. She cried every time she saw the tapping done.

Grandma asked the doctor, "Why can't it be me instead of her? I'm old, and she's so young. She still has eight children to raise."

The doctor could only shake his head and say, "I know."

Grandma would ride the train back home, sobbing out loud all the way.

Mother had to have the tapping done every two or three days. That's how long it took for her body to build up fluids. Without the tapping, she could die.

Our car became her lifeline.

Mom wouldn't let you know she suffered because she never complained. Priel shook her head and said, "That sister of mine never raises her voice." Priel came to help care for Mother and Freddy.

Every day I went to my mother's room to ask her how she was feeling.

She always smiled and said, "I'm a little better." Or, "I'm feeling fine."

Yet things were looking very bleak.

It was difficult for Mother to function. She could only walk for a day or so, then she was back in bed, swollen. She couldn't work, or eat much, or do anything except try to cope with her condition.

We were trying to cope too. Our life was growing stranger by the day. Everybody was fending for themselves.

Troy and I were fixing breakfast each morning, making bacon and eggs. My fried potatoes were actually edible.

Aunt Reva and Marvel came by to wash our clothes and clean house. Several women from the church offered to come and help, but Mother declined.

"I have all the help I need from Keith," she assured them. "He is so handy."

Mother was too independent. Aunt Priel was the only person who Mom called for help. Priel came and stayed for weeks while she and Grandma Shaw took care of Mother.

Mom was in so much pain, she needed peace and quiet. She was never cross, even when she needed us to keep the noise down. Our neighbor May Larson, a nurse, came by to give Mother shots for pain.

Dad made the girls stay in the kitchen most days, with the door closed. Barbara did her schoolwork. Helen and Ruth sat on the floor playing with dolls or drawing pictures.

Troy and Mert stayed outside helping Dad, avoiding the house or going off with their friends. I gave Floyd projects to work on out in the barn while I did chores.

As Mother waned, we passed the time around the kitchen table. The evenings were long, but we played games and listened to the radio. We listened to Fibber McGee and Molly—a comedy show about a man and his wife. Fibber always opened closet doors and everything fell out with crashes and bangs. Floyd, Barbara and Helen liked listening to Little Orphan Annie.

Meanwhile, Mother was entering her final stretch.

She exerted herself, determined to care for Freddy and Ruth. Miraculously, she was able to do that almost to the end. At times when it seemed she suffered near death, she would rise from her bed to care for Freddy.

In a few days it would be Christmas. Yet no one seemed to notice.

Dad had been so busy working and trying to manage, we hadn't even gotten a tree. And nobody thought about presents. My last fifty dollars went to pay for Mother's tapping treatments.

One morning a couple of days before Christmas, Dad decided he wasn't going to work at the post office.

"Let's go get a tree," he announced.

Mert, Floyd, and Barbara ran to get their coats and boots.

"Can Mom go with us?" Helen asked.

"No, honey, not this time," Dad responded.

Cutting our tree was a family expedition to Blacksmith Fork Canyon, where the land was covered with scrub oak and pine trees; it was like our private forest. The little kids always got snow in their boots, so Mother would take them back to the car for hot chocolate and to empty their shoes.

Today, we went without Mother. Driving up the winding road to Grandpa Yeates' land, we moved in slow motion, climbing snow-packed roads through crystal white hills dotted by dark green trees. Looking out our windows, we scrutinized each one to see which would be our tree.

"There, Dad!" Troy spotted one. "That bushy one looks good." It was a little shorter than the others, but healthy and full.

We parked our car on the road and jumped out, reveling in the freedom of running across untouched snow. Mert was making long tracks. I went looking for deer prints.

Dad took out his axe and followed Troy to the tree. They cut it down in just a few chops. Wood cracked as Troy pulled it off the stump. Then we loaded it into the trunk of the car, too bushy to close the lid.

Arriving back home, Barbara, Helen, and Ruth ran into Mother's room to tell her all about the tree. Troy and I carried it into the house.

Troy made a tree stand, using two-by-fours. At sixteen, he was a handy carpenter.

We stood the tree up just outside Mother's bedroom so she could see it through the doorway from her bed.

Mert strung it with popcorn, although he ate more than he strung. Floyd and Barbara hung aluminum decorations while we sang Christmas carols. Mother watched us from her bedroom.

When we were done, I sat in the living room, looking at our decorated tree. A big lopsided cardboard star that Floyd made in school perched on top. The tree was lit with twelve candle lights, one for every month of the year. Each candle was held by a tiny metal clamp on the end of a pine branch.

As I gazed at its beauty, I realized this tree was about the same height as Mother. How odd that of all the trees on that hill, we chose one her size.

Then a random thought from Sunday School crossed my mind. In the garden of Eden there were two trees. A tree of life. And a tree of knowledge—of good and evil. I decided our tree was like the latter—a symbol for the loss of paradise.

In the next room, my mother lay dying.

Sometime in the darkness of early morning, I woke to the sound of Freddy crying. Dad had already gone to the barn and Freddy needed constant attention, so I got up to check on him. Mother was bedridden now. She could no longer care for Fred.

Mother did not want to die. Yet she knew she couldn't fight it much longer. Nothing was changing the course of disease in her body. Cancer was taking her away.

She was awake, trying to sing Freddy back to sleep from the confines of her bed. I crossed the room and picked him up, holding his chubby body close.

"I'll walk him," I assured her, carrying him into the next room.

It was then Mother moved. Very carefully, she rolled over onto her stomach and slid her legs off the bed so they were hanging down on the floor.

She wanted to pray—on her knees.

The moment she began to speak, her body began shaking with sobs. She was begging for God's help.

"Dear God ... what about my children? What will happen to them?" she cried helplessly.

She finally let out her pent-up emotions, as if her heart were liquid. She was exhausted and pleading, sobbing on her bed.

"Please, God, help my sweet baby ... my poor little Freddy. I can't bear to leave him."

Her wan frame lay upon the bed, arms limp in front, her face flat upon the sheets. In this position she stayed, crying out every last feeling inside.

"Please, God ... help me."

The faint light of dawn began to move across the room. A peace came over her, softly, like a shadow.

There would be no reprieve. But, things would be alright.

"Blanche," she said aloud to herself.

She had an answer. She wept again, thanking God.

❧ SEVEN ❧
Christmas Eve

Christmas Eve finally arrived, like a crucial deadline. With it came the season's first snow.

From Easter to Christmas, my mother changed drastically. The two biggest religious holidays of the year were the two most tragic times of her life. I wondered if Mother found irony in Christmas, knowing that death was knocking at her door.

Mother was failing fast, suffering near-constant pain. When I'd look in on her, she was usually asleep. May came over three or four times a day to check on her and give her shots of morphine.

Today was a brilliantly sunny day. Light glinted off the crisp, new snow outside.

Grandma Shaw and Aunt Priel showed up at noon ready to cook dinner. They put a pork roast in the oven with baked potatoes.

I looked in on Mother. Dad was sitting with her. These days, he usually stayed around the house to be close by her side.

Mother was gazing at the ceiling. Then she looked over at me.

"Keith ... ask Priel and Grandma to come here."

"Sure," I said, then went to the kitchen.

"Mom wants to talk to you both," I told Priel.

They went to her bedroom. I stood outside the door, listening, wondering what was up.

Dad was sitting in the chair holding Mom's hand. Whatever was coming, it was ominous.

"Meb and I have decided to give Freddy to Blanche."

Priel and Grandma were speechless. They stood there, blinking.

"Are you sure?" Priel asked.

"I'm sure," Mother answered.

"Blanche aches for a baby," Dad explained sadly. "Meb thinks it's the best thing for Freddy."

"Blanche is the only one who can really take care of him," Mother reasoned.

Grandma Shaw and Priel knew she was right, yet they couldn't believe what they were hearing.

Then came another surprise.

"Blanche is coming to take Freddy today," Dad announced.

"On Christmas Eve?" Priel wondered. "What will the children think?"

"I don't want the boys or girls around. Can you get his clothes ready to go, Priel?" Mother asked.

Priel suddenly realized how hard this must be for Mother. She decided to make it easier for Mom, rather than ask questions.

"Don't you worry, Meb," Priel assured her. "I'll have him ready to go. And I'll keep the girls occupied."

"Thank you Priel," Mother breathed.

We had seen some awful days, but this was the saddest one.

Priel gathered Freddy's clothes and toys and put them in a little bag.

I was hanging around to see what I could do. Troy and Mert were outside sledding in fresh snow. Floyd was at the neighbors' throwing snowballs.

Grandma Shaw suggested that Priel take the girls out on the porch where it was sunny. It wasn't too cold and they could watch the kids sledding down the road.

About two o'clock Blanche and Budge drove up.

Blanche's mother was with them. Priel welcomed them at the front door. Leaving the girls for a minute, Priel let them inside.

"Are you really taking him today, Blanche?" Priel asked.

"Yes, I'm taking Freddy," Blanche confirmed.

Priel led them into the bedroom.

Freddy was asleep in his little wooden crib in the corner.

"Hello, Blanche … " Mother struggled to hold back the tears.

"Oh, Meb, don't cry. I'll bring him over every week so you can all see him," Blanche promised.

"That would be nice," Mother sighed.

"I'll love Freddy as if he were my own," Blanche promised. She knelt down by the bed to hug Mother close.

"You're like a sister to me," Blanche continued. They were crying in each other's arms.

"Thank you, Blanche," was all Mother could say.

Dad, Budge, and the mother-in-law were all wiping their eyes.

"I guess it's time," Dad said.

Freddy was wrapped up in a nice blue blanket, all ready to go. Dad placed him into Mother's arms, one last time.

Mother couldn't hold him very well. He was still asleep, his growing body resting against Mother's emaciated chest.

She kissed his pudgy cheeks. Then she nodded at Dad, tears streaming down her face.

Freddy stirred and woke up, yawning and looking at the people around him through groggy little eyes.

"Hi, Freddy," Blanche smiled as she lifted him in her arms. He gurgled and smiled back.

"We'd better get going," Budge announced. Dad handed him Freddy's bag.

"I'll call you tomorrow, Meb," Blanche promised.

Freddy thought he was having fun. He liked all the attention he was getting.

Mother knew Blanche would give him what no one else could. Blanche would raise him well.

After they left, it was much too quiet in the house. I paced the living room floor.

Priel went to the kitchen to check on dinner. Grandma Shaw was putting the roast onto a platter.

"I know Freddy got a good home," Priel said, wiping her eyes.

Troy and Mert came home as hungry as two bears.

When we all sat down to Christmas Eve dinner, Dad told the others about Freddy.

Freddy's departure struck an inner fear, deep inside us. It was strange to lose our baby brother, even though we knew he would be fine. And we wondered about ourselves.

"Will someone come and take me away too?" Ruth voiced the fear. Her question nearly broke Dad's heart.

"No, honey, you'll stay right here," he assured her.

I could see concern on the faces of my brothers and sisters, wondering who would look after us if our mother was going away.

In spite of the sunshine, it was a dark day.

Later, Dad took us all into Mother's room. She wanted to comfort us and explain why she gave Freddy to Blanche.

"Freddy is too little …" she began in a quivering voice.

Dad helped her out. "Freddy brought us joy and love that only a baby can bring; but he needs our care all the time."

"Freddy is my gift to Blanche," Mother finished.

I realized then, that Freddy was a blessing. He had been drawing out our attention and love, during a wrenching time in our lives.

"I'm sure Freddy will be fine," I offered.

The others didn't say much, still feeling a visceral uncertainty.

Dad decided to change the subject.

"Have you looked under the tree?" he asked us.

"Nope," Floyd ran out to check. We all followed him into the living room.

Under our tree were four presents from Grandma Shaw and Aunt Priel.

For Helen and Ruth, there was a small wooden table with two little chairs, so they could play "tea" with little cups and saucers.

Barbara got a china doll with delicate, painted features.

For Troy and me there were brand new, store-bought pants and shirts.

Mert and Floyd each got a baseball hat, along with a bat and ball. They were so jazzed they ran outside to play ball in the snow.

Ruth wanted to know where Mother's present was. She wandered into Mother's room and climbed up by her bed.

"Mama, what can I give you? Ruth asked

"You're all I want," Mom answered.

"But Mama, I gotta git you something," Ruth insisted.

Mom held her close, trying not to cry.

In the other room, we ate apple pie and talked about our fine gifts as it grew dark outside.

A full moon cast shadows on new snow. Crisp and beautiful, I heard it crunch under the weight of sleighs and automobiles.

In homes all around us, the holiday atmosphere peaked. Our church at the corner was hosting a Christmas party.

Yet for us, the night was cheerless. Our mother was lying in bed, too weak to sit up or walk.

Dad asked Brother Snow from the church to come and say a prayer with our family. We were in need of a blessing.

When he arrived, Dad gathered us into the bedroom so we could kneel around her bed. I remembered the time Mother prayed during that bad storm in November.

Tonight, it was Brother Snow who prayed by her bed.

"Dear Father, please help this family." He asked a special blessing upon each one of us. Then he reminded God to watch over Freddy.

"This mother is a loving soul, who wants nothing more than to care for her children." He closed with an earnest request that her illness be healed.

We stood around the room, silent.

Then my dad gave another prayer. I guess he felt the need for an extra appeal to God. He simply pleaded with God to spare our mother's life.

The girls all stood near the head of the bed. Their hands were clasped, heads bowed. I can say I felt the presence of God in the room.

Afterward, Dad and Brother Snow walked out onto our porch.

Dad sighed. "There are many things worse than death."

"I'm sure there are," Brother Snow agreed.

"Losing one's honor is worse than death ..." Dad was searching for meaning.

"I've learned to see death as something natural, just like being born," Brother Snow explained. "We are all going down that road, some day."

Dad knew he was right. He had watched helplessly as Mother had been moving closer to death for the past six months. Each time she lost new ground, she tried to struggle back, but failed.

Inside the house, Mother reclined on pillows, unable to stay awake. She closed her eyes.

Outside in the barn that night, new life was emerging. Brownie gave birth to four pups.

❧ EIGHT ❧
Goodbye

Father's and Brother Snow's prayers must have worked some, because Mother seemed renewed. She was determined to hold on through the holidays, her favorite time of year.

So she did.

The first thing she said Christmas morning was something so typical of her.

"One thing I regret—besides cancer—" she looked at father, "is that I can't cook Christmas dinner."

"I don't care about dinner," he said, holding her thin frame in his arms. He laid on the bed next to her for a long time that morning.

About noon, Aunt Reva and Grandma Yeates brought over a roasted chicken with stuffing.

"It's not as good as Meb's cooking," Reva apologized. "But we hope it tastes alright."

I made biscuits and Troy mashed potatoes. Barbara made the gravy. Our kitchen was strangely empty, for Christmas.

Mert was teasing Helen, so I told them to set the table. Floyd was working on a puzzle. Aunt Reva was playing with Ruth.

"Tell everyone to come eat while it's hot," Grandma said.

Mother disliked being bedridden, almost more than being sick. This was Christmas. She couldn't stand the thought of missing family dinner, especially today.

So she made a supreme effort, determined to have a holiday spirit in her home.

She decided to have Christmas dinner with the family.

"I want to get up," Mother said quietly.

"No, you're too weak to get up, Meb," Grandma warned her.

"Yes, I can," she said.

"Are you sure?" Dad asked her.

"Yes. I'm not staying in bed today," she announced. "I'm going to sit at the table."

Mom wanted to eat with the family.

Dad and I lifted Mom out of bed, her thin form rising up from the bedding until she was standing. Her arms reached out on either side, resting limply around our shoulders. We put our arms around her waist and slowly walked to the dining room together, a skeletal woman supported by two humbled men.

We sat her gently in a rocking chair at the head of the table. Her body seemed feeble against the backdrop of that broad chair.

We seven children took our places as Grandma and Reva squeezed in. Dad took his place at the other end, opposite Mom.

"Just let me be with you," she said weakly, barely able to sit up. "I can't miss Christmas dinner." She smiled, but it was more like a grimace.

We all sat looking at her—unable to move.

"What's wrong ... did Barbara burn the gravy?" she weakly joked.

Troy, Mert, Floyd, Barbara, and Ruth all laughed, grateful for a release. Dad smiled. Helen and I looked at each other.

Dad began to pray. "Father, we thank thee for this bountiful feast prepared by loving hands. We thank thee for allowing Mother to be with us this day ... help us ... " A lump was rising in his throat. "Amen."

We were having family dinner. For a moment we forgot Mom was dying. Her strategy had worked. We were momentarily cheered.

I began passing the potatoes while Dad cut the chicken. Grandma fixed a plate for Mother, with a spoonful of each item so she could try a taste. Of course, it was wishful thinking. For the past week Mother had taken only liquids.

Mother tried to eat a little, but she simply couldn't swallow. She recovered her composure and smiled.

Instead, she listened to us kids eat and chatter like normal, about silly things in general.

On some level, I think we sensed that this was our last meal together.

As dinner wound down, Mom was unable to remain sitting up. Dad and I hopped up from the table and slowly lifted her from the chair. This time Dad carried her in his arms back to bed.

After he laid her down in those weary sheets, she told him one thing.

"My greatest desire is to live ... and take care of my children," she finished.

"I know, Meb ... I know," Dad consoled.

Then she slept. For the rest of that night, and most of the following week, she was sleeping. She finally seemed to give herself permission to rest.

I think it was all she could do. When she was awake, she was in pain. I could see it on her face, in the way she strained and winced, panting for breath. I found it odd that she never cried out the agony. Morphine gave her rest and escape.

Everyone stayed away from her room, except for Dad and me. He needed to be near her. I needed to see her through the task of dying. I looked in on her every few hours. The only time she moved or spoke was when she was praying.

Above my mother's bed on the wall were the words of a poem she loved. She had asked Dad to frame it and hang it on her wall, years before. The title was, "Her Gift."

"So wee a gift, yet wealth of many lands, could never buy it in the richest marts. So frail a gift, and yet those baby hands take mighty hold upon two human hearts."

Under that picture, my mother spent her final days, sleeping.

♣　♣　♣

A week later, on New Year's Day, some women from the church offered to fix dinner. When those ladies said they were bringing dinner, they were serious. They cooked as if they were feeding the whole church, arriving with baked ham, scalloped potatoes, salads, rolls, and pie.

Grandma Yeates stayed with us all day, and Grandma Shaw came over in the early evening. They knew Mom was failing and they wanted to be near her. At the same time, nobody wanted to hover over her, staring at her in the bed.

We children were torn—between our need to cling to Mother as she faded, and our need to avoid seeing her go. I don't think Mert and Troy wanted to see it happen. They stayed entertained elsewhere.

After dinner, the adults were talking in the kitchen while the younger kids played inside. I went to see how Mother was doing.

She was lying on the bed with her eyes closed. I noticed that she was praying. I stepped closer to listen.

I felt like a priest waiting to hear a confession, ready to hear anything she might say.

What I heard surprised me. I tell it now, to share what I learned.

Faintly, she was saying, "I'm sorry ... so sorry ... forgive me."

I was curious. What was she sorry for?. She seemed to be talking to herself.

Then she said, "I forgive you."

Who was she forgiving, I wondered?

"I forgive you," she said again, between stifled sobs.

"... for not living."

It took me awhile to realize what was happening. She wasn't talking to God. Mother was talking to herself. She was forgiving herself, I guess for not being strong enough to live. And maybe for the opposite as well—for trying too hard all those years.

I stood amazed and watched her accept the reality of her condition, finally relaxing into it. She was making peace with her cancer. She was becoming one with herself.

The enemy had been her own body, but how could she hate that? She had to embrace her enemy, to find healing in her soul.

The feeling in the room was beyond words.

It was then I recognized a powerful truth: when we finally embrace the finite nature of our physical being, we begin to see its spiritual dimension.

I left her alone with her self-confession.

May came by at six o'clock to give Mother another shot. She noticed that Mom was laboring to breathe, and spoke privately to Dad.

Impending death permeated the air.

All seven of us children sat silently in the living room. Grandma Shaw and Grandma Yeates were with Mother.

Each of us was lost in our own emotions. Sadness, anxiety, confusion. And one dominating question.

Why? We didn't understand. Never had we questioned life until this moment. It was a terrible new feeling.

We labored under a heavy, heavy dread—without the maturity to handle such intense feelings.

About eight o'clock, Dad led us into Mother's room.

She lay motionless on the bed. As we gathered around her, she looked at each one of us.

In a feeble voice she said, "I love you ..."

Helen and Ruth were clinging to her side.

She looked at Dad. "Take care of them, Leo ..."

"I will, Meb," Dad wept.

She was so weak, it was hard for her to speak. But she managed to leave us with her love.

All of us were crying, except for ten-year-old Barbara. She was in too much pain to cry.

We each hugged her as gently as we could. I kissed her and said "I love you, Mom."

And then we went to bed. In many ways, it was a night like so many others. She lay quietly in her bedroom as we moved away to spare her more worry or pain.

About ten o'clock, Dad woke us boys up.

"Come to Mother's room," he said urgently.

I went to wake the girls. Ruth was sleeping peacefully. Barbara and Helen jumped out of bed.

Dad gathered us back to her bedside and knelt down beside her, holding her hand. We all stood around her bed, watching.

She was straining to breathe. Her skin looked pastel white. She was lying there death-like, not even moving.

Suddenly, my father fell across her bed, clutching her arms tightly and cried out, "Don't leave us, Meb! Stay with us—don't go!"

He was frantic, calling her back.

She opened her eyes and looked at him. She tried to smile, but couldn't. It was too much effort.

Then she began to breathe, first rasping, heavy, then lighter. She opened her eyes to look at Dad, then closed them again, over and over.

We went back to our beds. May stayed at Mother's side along with Dad.

After that, Mother hung on two or three hours. She stayed, because Dad begged her to stay.

Dad remained by her side every minute. Kneeling over her body, holding her in his arms, he stroked her dark hair.

"I love you, Meb," he said, trying to keep her with him.

Finally Mother struggled to breathe one last time. And stopped.

It was half past midnight, on January 2nd.

Dad collapsed, weeping uncontrollably, holding her frail body in his arms, still warm.

May called the doctor, who came and pronounced my mother dead.

She was 40 years old.

In the early morning just after dawn, Dad woke us children to tell us she was gone.

The moment was surreal. We got out of bed slowly and walked to her bedroom to stand around her bed, one last time.

Mother looked so peaceful. There was no more pain. Her skin was porcelain white.

Troy and Mert were stone-faced, unable to speak or move. Floyd and Helen stood by, looking scared.

Barbara still couldn't cry. She had a huge lump in her throat. It just swelled in her chest and stayed there for days.

I stood looking at Mom's tiny, lifeless frame and wept—one of a hundred times for my mother's loss.

Later that morning, Lindquist and Sons Mortuary came to take her body. Mr. Lindquist and his oldest boy wrapped Mother's body in a white sheet. Lifting her off the bed, they laid her onto a stretcher.

As they carried her outside to the long, gray hearse, we all followed. We boys watched in total silence. The girls were crying and hanging on to Dad. Mr. Lindquist opened up the back of his hearse and slid her body inside. Then he closed the door.

That's when the grief really hit me. Like never before. They were taking my mother away. She would never come back.

For the first time, I panicked. I ran out past the hearse and straight down the road, as fast as my legs could go. Running in the winter, without my coat. I just wanted to get away.

❧ NINE ❧
A Return

No one felt like celebrating the New Year.

Ruth cried for Mama every day after she died. Barbara tried to comfort her, then at night, cried herself to sleep.

Helen was scared. Whenever someone mentioned the word "death" it frightened her, wondering who was going to die next.

Mert and Floyd stayed busy outside, doing chores or sledding the hill at Millville Park. Every once in a while they would think of Mom and I could see their heads droop, their shoulders slump.

Troy and I kept a stiff upper lip, doing the milking and feeding the animals. When our emotions swelled, we'd go out into the barn or climb the haystack, to be alone.

There is no such thing as the holidays without Mother. There is no such thing as life without Mother. We didn't know how to *be* without her. We were lost, like Brownie's newborn puppies, their eyes not yet opened—crying and crawling in the dark, slipping and stumbling in a strange, enormous new world.

Blanche called and invited us to her house for supper. Nobody felt like eating. We were too numb.

Another ordeal was waiting—the funeral. On January 6, 1939, we buried our mother.

The Lindquist Mortuary returned her body to us, laid in a dark brown coffin. They placed a spray of white flowers across our front door.

Mother's casket rested in our front room. For two hours that morning, relatives and friends came through our home to pay Mother their last respects.

Each person stood by her casket looking at her delicate beauty. She was lying on puffy white pillows that reminded me of clouds.

Aunt Priel and Grandma Shaw kept saying how young my mother looked. So tiny and pretty, like a girl.

"My poor Meb," Grandma cried, "so sweet and precious."

"She looks just like a china doll," Priel lamented.

Someone gave Helen a wreath of flowers for Mother's grave. She thought they were for the funeral, so she walked up to the church and waited there. We looked all over the house for her. Finally Reva noticed Helen sitting alone up at the church, holding that wreath for Mother.

Everyone came to Mother's funeral. Nibley church was packed full with people from Logan to Magna. Mom would have been surprised by all the attention she got.

It was a bitterly cold, grey January day. The wind was swirling a fine powder of snow. Not the kind of day most folks want to go out. By twelve noon, a hundred people had parked in front of the church and were talking inside the foyer.

As I sat down in the pew, I wondered if Grandpa Fred ever knew his family would have their funerals here in the church he helped build. He and Grandma had lived next door for 40 years; when Grandpa died, we had his funeral in this chapel.

Today, it was Mother's turn. People were buzzing in the foyer, feeling a need to express their feelings. Mother's death made no sense to anyone. Women were saying it just wasn't fair—she was such a good woman. Men were offering their sympathy to Dad and asking him about the farm.

Blanche and Budge were there with Freddy. It was strange to see him with another family. Excited to be with him, we insisted on taking turns holding him. We all sat together on the front row.

All of my mother's sisters were there, sitting with Grandma Shaw. They were beside themselves with grief over Mother's death at such a young age. They were sobbing all through the funeral.

At 1:00 p.m. the service started. Uncle Eugene gave the invocation,

"Father, we are surrounded with relatives and friends to pay our last earthly respect to one of thy sisters whom Thou has called home ... Look down on my brother in his time of trial and sorrow and give him strength and courage ..."

His last line intrigued me: "And bless us to live so that the spirits of our loved ones will be near to us."

Grandpa's brother, Uncle Alma, spoke. He voiced an observation that everyone noticed about Mother.

"I have never in my life heard Melba criticize or speak evil of anyone. That is more than I can say for myself. I am sure Meb is happy," he assured us.

Brother Snow talked about Mom's complete selflessness and her determination to live for her family. He eulogized, "I have never seen greater faith and courage. She never complained."

While my Uncle Carl gave the benediction, one thought kept haunting me. I wondered if somehow my mother had been *too* good. If somewhere in all her selfless giving, there should have been some selfishness, too.

The grayish day was as dreary as death itself. After the funeral, we got into our new car and drove behind the hearse, leading a line of cars out to Millville cemetery.

At the family plot, in a space off by itself, the men lowered my mother's casket into her grave. We didn't stay to see it covered with dirt.

Dad drove us to Logan so we could be with Fred. We needed to be with him and kiss his chubby face.

Freddy never saw so much attention. We all tried to hold him at once. Troy and Mert were swinging him high in the air until he giggled himself silly. The girls nearly kissed the skin off his cheeks.

"Freddy seems happy," Dad said to Blanche, his eyes brimming. "Meb was right—you're the best mom he could have."

"I love him like he was my own," Blanche said.

When we arrived home, everyone was too sad and tired to say much. We just wanted to lie down and go to sleep. Dad was feeling really low.

When Mom was dying, Dad had focused on the tasks in front of him, one thing at a time. Work helped him forget death or ease the pain, for a moment. Then the dread would come back again, hard, like a relapse of the flu.

Forget. Remember. Try to forget. Remember. Six times in one hour, until another hour crawled by. That was how he had kept going for months. If he sat down for very long, the sadness would engulf him.

Night time was the worst—when he was alone with it. There was no escape; no place to go. There was nothing to do, but lie there and face it.

That's when the feeling overtook him. Alone in bed, in the dark. Grief came to him every night, like a ghost. And he relented, letting it take him. He gave in, burying his face in the pillow so we kids wouldn't hear him sobbing. He was so tired he usually fell asleep that way—exhausted, spent.

Tonight after the funeral was harder. The reality of Mom's death finally came down on him. That feeling when there's no place to go. Just you, facing yourself, totally alone, with no way out. Mom was really gone. The holidays without her. The house without her. The kids without her. A new year without her. A life without her.

The sense of loss was swallowing him. He couldn't sleep. He was crying so hard he was making himself sick. He feared he might break under the weight of it all. For the first time in his life, he wanted to die.

In despair, he cried out to her.

"Meb, why did you have to go? We need you so much. Please don't leave me, Meb …"

There was nothing else to do. It was all he had left.

His love and need for her.

And then that feeling of absolute love or need welled up inside of him, burning like a fire. Meb was gone, but his need for her still burned. It was his only connection to her. Somehow it brought her back, until he could almost feel her presence.

Just realizing this made the feeling grow stronger. Warmer. Bigger. It was burning in the pit of his stomach—like glowing heat from hot embers, swelling to fill him. He didn't know what was happening. He wondered if he was getting sick. If so, he didn't care.

Then it suddenly engulfed him—the heat of his emotion, love. It was inside him, yet much bigger, glowing beyond his body, consuming the room. It felt as if it would consume the whole house, maybe even the whole county. He didn't know what was happening. He was radiating like the sun.

And then she was there.

He could see her. Standing at the foot of his bed, a moving mist of warm white glow, with features. Her image was a shimmering impression of light, breathing the air.

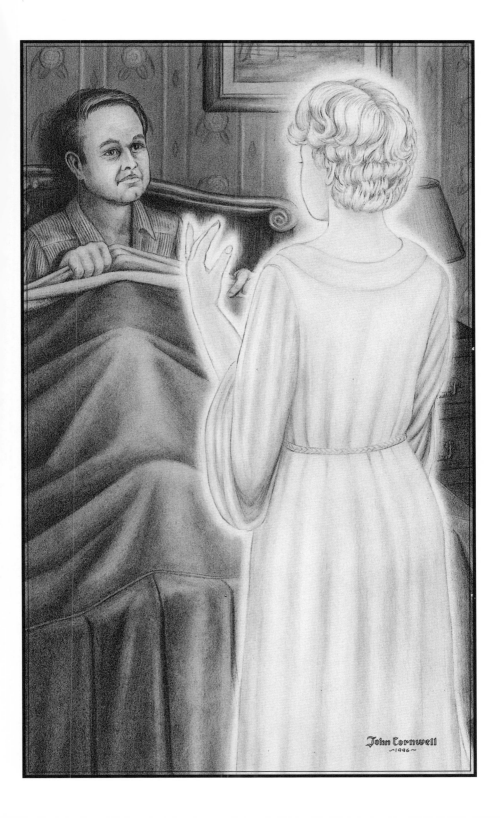

John Cornwell
~1996~

He thought he was imagining it. All the stress was making him see things. Yet the feeling was real, permeating right through him and all around him. He could feel and see her presence at the same time. It was impossible to explain. She and the feeling were one, emanating, bathing right through him.

Meb.

She was smiling. So happy, free of all cares and pain.

She paused, then smiled at him again.

A wave of comfort passed over him, bringing perfect peace. He could not describe how it felt. He seemed to be flowing in all directions at once, becoming a new being.

She paused again. Then smiled at him, one last time.

Forever.

Then her image faded. She never said a word.

He wept openly. Thankful sobs came from the center of his soul. It was a complete release.

She had kept the promise they made six years before. She came back to let him know she was alright.

The children were asleep. I lay awake and could hear the sounds of sobbing in his room.

✃ TEN ✃
God's Greatest Gift

Sunrise on Sunday morning was unusually bright for January. A palette of yellow, pink, and pale orange pastel light glowed over the horizon, reflecting on the clouds above the mountains. Troy, Dad, and I walked to the barn in silence, staring at a glorious sky.

Back in the house, Barbara was making pancakes for breakfast and Floyd was helping her.

When we walked in, the pancakes were burning, so I took over. Dad and Troy hung their milking boots in the closet next to the kitchen then sat in the dining room.

"Are we going to Aunt Priel's?" Helen asked, holding Ruth on her lap.

"I miss Mommy," Ruth whimpered. Dad reached over and picked her up, putting her onto his lap.

"Don't cry, honey," Dad comforted.

"Where's Mommy?" Ruth bawled.

"Mommy's watching over us," Dad consoled her.

"Really Dad?" Helen asked.

"Yes, she can see us," he assured her.

"Why can't we see her?" Helen asked.

"Because she lives in the light," he said quietly.

"Where?" Helen asked.

He had a blissful expression on his face for the first time in months.

"There's something I need to tell you," he said calmly.

All of a sudden the room grew very still, like the feeling you get at church.

Dad told Barbara and me to come into the dining room. We put our pancakes in the oven to stay warm.

There with the seven of us sitting around the dining table, my father described our mother's visit to him the night before. How she had appeared as an emanation of light, standing at the foot of his bed.

As he confided his experience, he was baring his soul. We had never seen him so vulnerable. He opened himself completely, bringing us into his heart. Tears ran down his face, his eyes shining. His heart seemed healed.

We were in awe, unable to speak. We just listened. Barbara looked stunned, holding Ruth who sat quietly. Helen put her head and arms down onto the table and wept. We boys were utterly silent.

Finally, after a few minutes, I spoke.

"I think Mother had a message," I said, wiping my eyes with my sleeve.

"What is it?" Helen asked, her eyes swollen red.

"Her smile," I responded, "was everything she needed to say."

"I don't get it," Mert said, sniffling.

Dad had a knowing look in his eyes.

"Her smile means love," Dad said.

We sat at the table where she had fed us, every day of our lives. The power and spirit of her irrepressible love were still so strong, we were filled.

This experience altered our perspective of her death. Instead of grieving for her absence, we felt gratitude for her life. That she had lived, that her spirit still lived, gave us a something of her presence in our lives.

I realized then how life is a gift.

If we think about Mother's absence more than her life, we take her life for granted. That is something she never did. She lived every day to the fullest. If we think about Mother's life, more than her absence, then we appreciate her.

I found myself wondering, what if she had never lived? Or only lived to age 20? or 30? At what point should her life have ended? At what point would her life be fulfilled? Do we value the life we have already lived, as much as the life we hope to yet live?

Life is a gift. Mother's life was a temporary treasure to be valued for itself.

Even in death she helped us. Our bleak emptiness was altered by the miracle of her reappearance. It was something we never expected—a reunion, another gift.

The next day, we tried to go back to our normal routine.

January 1939 was a new year, a new life.

1938 had brought so much suffering, pain, and loss. Yet, in the end, it blessed us with a miraculous resolution. What a perplexing, paradoxical year, full of intense transition.

Looking back, our tragic year seemed like a harbinger of much larger events. Other happenings in the world hinted at coming changes or loss.

In December 1938, Rose Kennedy was selected the "Outstanding Woman of the Year." Howard Hughes was the "Outstanding Aviator." Amelia Earheart was preparing for her flight around the world. Adolf Hitler was *TIME* magazine's "man of the year." Leni Riefenstahl debuted her Nazi film, "The Triumph of the Will." Germany was poised to invade Europe. World War II waited just over the horizon in 1939.

Yet we were occupied by our own losses.

Dad was getting ready to leave for Logan when he heard someone knocking at the door. He was still working at the post office.

He answered the door.

"Good day, sir!" a plump, cheery-faced man in a wool suit grabbed my dad's hand.

"What can I do for you?" Dad offered.

"My name is Wendell … I understand you've recently had a death in the family," he said, more gently.

"Yes," Dad said quietly.

"Well," he began slowly, "do you have a nice headstone for your wife?"

"No," Dad answered. "We didn't have money to get one."

"Well, sir, I have some lovely headstones for bargain prices," the man assured him.

"How did you know about us?" Dad queried.

"I read the obituaries," he answered.

"What are your prices?" Dad ventured.

"I have three beautiful styles. I can show you and your family a nice photo of each one and let you choose," he smiled.

"Okay, come on in," Dad agreed.

Wendell the salesman was carrying a small, brown suitcase. He looked around in the dining room and said, "Let me lay these pictures on your table so you can all see them."

We followed him to the dining table and took a seat. He opened his bag and pulled out three large black and white photographs. Each was a close-up shot of a granite gravestone with an inscription carved into the face and a decorative outline of foliage or design.

He held up the first one. "This is my favorite. It says, 'The Lord is My Shepherd—He Restoreth My Soul.'" Underneath the words was a carved image of a small sheep resting in grass.

He let us pass the photo around the table so we could each see it up close. Then he held up the next one.

"This is our most popular stone: 'Our Beloved Mother—Among the Angels.'" It had a carved outline of two angels with wings. I looked at it, thinking about my father's description of Mother, standing in the light. She didn't have wings.

Then he held up the last one. "Isn't this precious? It says, 'God's Greatest Gift, Returned to God.'" Small flowers curled around the bottom. As the photo of this headstone went around the table, our eyes welled up with tears. Wendell could see this was the right one.

"How much are they?" Dad asked again, wiping his eye.

"They're normally $75," Wendell confessed, looking awkward with all eight of our sad faces around him. He quickly added, "But I'll sell you one for $50."

Dad had little money and so many bills to be paid. Yet he really wanted Mother to have a nice headstone.

"I'm afraid all I have is thirty dollars," he said.

At that moment I vowed I would make enough money to pay off our debts.

Wendell looked guilty and said, "That's fine, sir—I'll take thirty for it. You need a nice marker for your wife."

"Okay then, we'll take it." Dad got up and went into the bedroom where he had the money in a drawer. He came back in and handed the salesman three ten-dollar bills.

"You'll deliver the stone to her grave?" Dad asked.

"Oh yes, of course. We'll take care of everything," Wendell nodded enthusiastically. "We'll place it into the ground. You just meet us this afternoon and show us the right plot."

"What time?" Dad said.

"How about five o'clock? Just keep this receipt in case anything goes wrong," he said shaking Dad's hand.

"All right then," Dad half smiled. "I'll see you at five."

Wendell walked out onto the porch, then he turned to say, "And bring your family with you, so they can see it." Then he left.

This gave Dad time to put in a day's work at the post office. Troy and I had chores. We all tried to stay busy, but we couldn't wait to see the headstone for our mother's grave.

About two o'clock Aunt Reva came by with an envelope for Dad.

"He won't be back 'til about five o'clock," I explained. "We're going to the cemetery—to put a headstone on Mother's grave."

"That's wonderful; I'll go with you," Aunt Reva smiled.

"What's in the envelope?" Mert asked.

Reva wouldn't say what it was. She just looked sad-eyed. "It's a surprise," she said.

I didn't know what to think. Was it bad news or good?

While Reva waited for Dad to return, she cleaned the kitchen and put a roast into the oven for dinner.

When Dad returned at four thirty, Aunt Reva took him aside and whispered something we couldn't hear. He looked stunned.

He asked, "Do you want to come with us to her grave?"

Reva nodded. By a quarter to five, we were all in the Plymouth, heading to the cemetery.

When we arrived, Wendell was not around, but a workman was there, waiting with the headstone to place on Mother's grave.

Dad showed him which one was hers. Then we stood and watched as he set her headstone, brushing dirt from the edges. A brownish granite marker with delicate flowers and inscription rested firmly in place.

It was perfect.

We stood around her grave in a circle, gazing quietly at the headstone. I was holding Ruth.

Then Aunt Reva took out the envelope and opened it.

She handed a piece of white stationery to Dad. He read it for a few minutes. Then he handed it back to her, tears in his eyes.

It was a letter from Mother to us.

Reva read the words out loud, so we could all hear.

"My dear children:

I'm sorry I had to leave you. I don't want to go. But God has other plans for me.

"I love you. I will always love you.

"I don't want you to feel alone after I'm gone. Please know that I will be watching over you, from heaven.

"Daddy loves you as much as I do. He is there whenever you need him. Love him as much as you can.

"Your aunts love you, too. They will look after you and help you.

"Be good for Mommy. Do your best in school. Be sure to dress warmly when you go out into the snow.

"Always remember, God loves you. He hears your prayers. Don't forget to say your prayers at night.

"I will miss you my good boys. Keith. Troy. Mert. Floyd. And my sweet little girls: Barbara. Helen. Ruth. And my dear little Freddy. Please love each other and help each other.

"I will love you forever.

"Mother."

Reva folded the paper, and put it back into the envelope.

Mother had dictated the letter to Aunt Reva, weeks before she died.

We were speechless, lost in our feelings. We stood weeping around her grave.

Then Dad read the inscription on Mother's headstone.

"Melba ... Harriet ... Shaw ...," he said the words slowly, out loud.

"God's ... Greatest ... Gift. Returned ... to God."

"It's beautiful, Leo," Reva said.

"The greatest gift is a mother," he said, "because she gives us life."

I thought about it and guessed he was right. Life's greatest sacrifices are those of a parent for a child.

But what about the gift of knowledge—the grace and wisdom of a spiritual vision like my father's?

And what about the gift of peace—like my mother felt just before she died? When she let go of guilt and accepted herself in failure. Of all that my mother accomplished in her 40 years, her hardest work may have been the gift of mercy to herself.

Is mercy God's greatest gift?

I wondered. Is God's greatest gift happiness? What about loss and suffering? We learn so much from pain.

Is God's greatest gift life? Or life after death?

I valued my mother's life. Yet her death had brought other gifts, too.

Mother's death gave me insight, and taught me that suffering and evil will enter our lives, no matter what we do. Her death taught me the lessons of loss.

And her suffering brought wisdom. Mother's suffering showed how the good and bad strive together in life.

Cancer was such a negative presence, so opposite of Mom's nature. It seemed as destructive, as she was benevolent. Removing the cancer failed to stop it. Perhaps such a disease cannot be healed. Yet I know my mother found healing in her soul, the night she forgave herself for not succeeding.

I cherished her act of self-forgiveness which taught me mercy and redemption. Maybe the greatest gift is redemption.

A great soul is one who rises above the mundane nature of life and touches the divine—beyond this crude, material world.

My mother had touched the infinite. Then like a voice between worlds, she conveyed the divine back to us.

She gave us life—then she gave us a glimpse of what lies beyond it. Her reappearance taught me love. It gave me hope that life and love continue.

When the person you love most dies, you learn one thing: that love is what matters. If we can show our love, maybe we have mastered life. Perhaps love is God's greatest gift.

I pondered all these gifts. As these thoughts turned in my head, I couldn't decide which gift was God's greatest.

Before Mother was sick, we assumed life would always be the same. She would cook Sunday dinner and we would be filled, with her food and her love. Life with Mother would continue year after year as we grew older and had families of our own.

We did go on to have many good times in the years ahead. Yet on each holiday, at each family gathering, we wondered if she was there, watching us, smiling.

I always had the feeling she was.

❧ EPILOGUE ❧

After Mother died, we went in different directions for awhile. Mert, Floyd, and the girls took turns living with my aunts.

Troy and I worked on the farm until 1940. We managed to pay off most of the bills, including the balance on our Plymouth. Then I joined the army and Troy went to college in Logan. Eventually, all four of us boys served in the war and returned.

When I came home from the war in '46, I helped Dad work our farm. He eventually remarried and I got married, too. Faye and I moved into a house up the road from Dad. I guess we wanted to keep an eye on my younger brothers and sisters.

In spite of Mother's absence in our lives, we managed to find our own way. Freddy grew up and became a barber like Budge; in fact he still runs the barber shop in Logan. We are a determined, hardworking lot, thriving on the Wasatch Front, seeking our dreams. Anyone could say we have succeeded.

Yet I've come to realize that success is more than getting ahead, more than finding the kind of life we desire. Success can come to the poor or uneducated as well as to the privileged—because it happens within ourselves. Real success is a mysterious place, hiding in that precarious balance where we strive alone, between life's good and bad.

Today, the Great Depression is either a dim memory, or an unfathomable disaster. Yet we lived through it and survived, even having good times. I believe it's possible to avoid such a calamity, or to thrive in spite of it.

Economy and peace are forever teetering. History can always repeat itself. If we face another great depression or war, it will be because we need to learn those lessons again. Yet even in the worst turmoil, those simple truths I found the year my mother died continue to guide me.

I learned life's true value from my Mother's death. The purpose of life is to live each moment fully, valuing experience for what it is, instead of what it should be. Taking nothing for granted, life asks us to value every person, encounter, every moment as a gift. Our existence is the chance to be alive and experience all of it.

Mother's death changed the way I lived, giving me a more pragmatic perspective. Had I never experienced her loss, I would not have treasured my life or time with my own children as much. I learned to expect less from others, and to appreciate everything more.

I have benefitted from Mother's terrible lessons, perhaps in ways she never did. I don't try to do everything, nor do I live for guilt or others' expectations.

And the bad parts of life? I value them for what they teach me. Mother's suffering taught me to work with negative things, to accept the bad gifts, and find their hidden meanings. They are places where darker angels reside, but angels nonetheless.

This year, breast cancer will invade 178,700 women in this country, and 43,500 will die. Each story is as real as my mother's; each life, an irreplaceable gift. Each struggle is a solitary quest for redemption.

This Christmas is the 60th anniversary of my mother's death. It's hard to believe our family has visited her grave for six decades.

Mother's resting place still bears the headstone my father bought from the traveling salesman. It's a 90-minute drive north of Salt Lake. Beyond Brigham City, Highway 89 winds over the mountains into Cache Valley, becoming the road to Logan. It passes by Nibley and Millville where a humble cemetery graces the eastern slopes.